16 WEEKS

AND

EVERYTHING

AFTER

PAUL WHYMARK

Matador
9 Priory Business Park,
Wistow Road, Kibworth Beauchamp,
Leicestershire. LE8 0RX
Tel: 0116 279 2299
Email: books@troubador.co.uk
Web: www.troubador.co.uk/matador
Twitter: @matadorbooks

ISBN 978 1788033 749

British Library Cataloguing in Publication Data.
A catalogue record for this book is available from the British Library.

Printed on FSC accredited paper
Printed and bound in Great Britain by 4edge Limited

Typeset in 11.5pt Calibri by Troubador Publishing Ltd,
Leicester, UK
The book is produced in a sans serif font to help improve
access for people with visual reading challenges.
In an e-book format it may be possible to customize reader
interface for text and back ground.

Matador is an imprint of Troubador Publishing Ltd

For my mother, Margaret 1939 to 2005

And

All mothers given whichever pharmaceutical drug(s) during
pregnancy that left their babies harmed
or impaired at any level

Photograph: Paul looking after his mother Margaret

If you found information in the book of interest please
share; and together we can raise the profile for establishing
transparency concerning harms caused by drugs/
medication consumed during pregnancy

The Ethos of Paul's Shed

Appreciate how changing the world starts with bite-size pieces

Go after one piece at a time

Work when and where you can to take things forward

Share with open minded and sincere people, they need you also

Always operate with fairness and consideration

No political management speak in the shed, there's no space

Generate new ideas by finding answers to questions not yet asked

Stimulate by contact with nature and the environment

Aim for simplicity in outcome and process

Evaluate and rethink if needed, but never give up

Eventually your time will come

(Photography support: Mark & Julie shed provision).

"16 Weeks and Everything After..." ©

Or alternatively
"Information you always had the right to know about Thalidomide, but were not previously informed"

Written in accordance with *The Ethos of Paul's Shed*

An unstoppable force of nature

"The pen is mightier than the sword"
Edward G. Bulwer–Lytton (1839)

"Photography with word processing (plus spell-check) is a good alternative"
Paul (2014)

Contents

Wholesome contents are essential for the next generation

Acknowledgements and Appreciation	xi
Foreword	xi
Introduction	xiii
I The Conscious Informs the Subconscious	1
"Your Hands and Your Feet!"	3
Rebuilding Noah's Ark on a Coastal Footpath	17
Growing Concerns	26
II Deeper Realisations	41
In the Deep End and Tri-ing new things	43
Dairy or Diary?	52
Mapping Connections by Connection Mapping	60

Chasing Dragonflies and a Trip Back to 1968/ 69   73

Unanswered Questions in Australia   82

III A Greater and Wider Awareness   95

Joining up Unseen Dots...   97

A Phone Call for Help out of a National Park   106

Notable Connections at Aberdeen   121

Life is Stranger than Fiction   138

A Bolt out of a Blue Sky   147

IV Shining Daylight into Some Very Dark Corners   161

Finally Coming Home Via Hollywood and Colorado   163

Nature Never Hides or Misrepresents Anything   171

A Corporate Garden Path   182

Some Help from April fools   208

V Turning Negatives into Positives   221

A Heroine, plus Betsy Andreu's good example   223

A Zeitgeist Lens for Action   232

Knowledge Sharing   246

C. S. R. – Having Cake and Eating It?   265

The Road Ahead...   286

Post Script and Authors Note   293

Appendix   295

Information Materials, Bibliography and References   297

Acknowledgments and Appreciation

Good things can and do happen

The Field Studies Council (F.S.C.) at Preston Montford provided transferable input from environmental and ecological education. The concept of producing a book emerged during a conversation with Andrea McNichol in 2013. Support and feedback came from many other people along the way and included; Ross and Bill Shell, Philip Taylor, Mark and Jenni Duffel, David and Jennifer Veale plus family, Denise Murray–Mason along with her family and wider social community. At various times and levels a range of further editing assistance/ contributions came from: Guy Woodford a Malvern Sculptor, Malvern Writers

Circle (founded in 1948), especially Linda Edkins Blackett and John Xzavian; Editor and Ecologist, Alex Morss, plus Rita Carter of Oxford Editors. Literary agent Kizzy Thomson offered feedback and helpful publishing suggestions, and others also provided general assistance.

The key information was shared by my mother, Margaret, and is central to the underlying quest of *"16 Weeks and Everything After..."©*. Thanks to all, Paul.

Foreword

This book *"16 Weeks and Everything After..."©* is written from the perspective of all *Thalidomide* survivors, and of survivors of other drugs that may have harmed developing human life during pregnancy. This is regardless of whether or not people have been recognised and acknowledged as being harmed by *Thalidomide* or another drug. The full extent and range of harms caused by *Thalidomide* goes far further than has previously been officially accepted, and this maybe the case for other drugs also. All the same *"16 Weeks and Everything After..."©* considers all *Thalidomide* and all other pregnancy drug survivors equal in human terms.

My journey of self-discovery, discovery and wider societal illumination is part of the legacy of all *Thalidomide* survivors, and also survivors of all other drugs that may have caused harm in pregnancy. We all have the right to have a voice, and to establish full transparency concerning safety of all drugs consumed during pregnancy, both old and new. In addition it is right to speak up to prevent future drug harms being inflicted in the most vulnerable and defenceless stages of human life.

Introduction

In the mid to late 1950's a German drug company Chemie Grünenthal, developed the drug *Thalidomide* for the consumer market. Grünenthal sold their active ingredient *Thalidomide* to other drug companies that used it to produce a range of *Thalidomide* products in various forms including; capsules, tablets and syrup solutions. In the UK, Distillers Company Bio-chemicals Ltd (a subsidiary of the Distillers Company Ltd) used *Thalidomide* procured from Grünenthal in an assortment of products including Distaval, Distaval Forte, Valgraine, Asmaval, Tensival and others.

Thalidomide was a drug looking for a purpose, not the other way around. It started use as a sedative, and then moved to psychiatric medicine for anxiety and mild depression. From there it soon became used for many other medical purposes. Notably this included use for morning sickness, despite woefully inadequate testing for risks of harm to the unborn. *Thalidomide* was promoted as *"atoxic"* and *"completely safe"*, to the extent it was claimed it was impossible to overdose. These assurances were totally false, as the drug could and did produce serious side effects in healthy adults, while in developing babies it left a wide range of harms and malformations; many of which have still not been officially recognised, acknowledged or in many cases even perceived as possible until considering the information in this book.

By the early 1960's some in the medical profession began to have serious concerns, in relation to a troubling increase in the numbers of babies being born, with significantly reduced and damaged limbs. It gradually became evident the rise in such cases were due to consuming the drug *Thalidomide* during pregnancy.

Around 1962 *Thalidomide* began to no longer be recommended for use during early pregnancy. Although a great deal of controversy continued as to what constituted *Thalidomide* harms and injuries. The *Thalidomide* drug companies, notably Grünenthal and Distillers Company (Bio-Chemicals) Ltd, then engaged in hostile rancorous and protracted standoffs, against a limited number of families who struggled to pursue legal action.

Meanwhile governments passively stood back and did little or nothing. Poor enforcement of existing regulations continued, while it was years before other regulations improved. Testing on *Thalidomide* to establish what and if any limits of harm existed, was not adequately conducted or co-ordinated.

Social injustice continued with people affected by *Thalidomide* then being suppressed by corporate might and government inaction. As a result not all the issues were satisfactorily aired, and much less dealt with. This was both despite and in part due to restrictions that limited reporting of information, while legal proceedings continued up to 1976. Thereafter the victors, the *Thalidomide* drug companies and governments, got to write with a free hand their airbrushed version of history, without ever having to acknowledge inconvenient realities.

This established an inaccurate and erroneous narrative concerning what constituted *Thalidomide* harm from exposure during pregnancy. It facilitated denial of people who were negatively affected by *Thalidomide*, but at stages during pregnancy they deemed not to recognise. Yet further barriers were erected by decreeing *Thalidomide* harms could only occur during a handful of select days within the first 9 weeks of pregnancy.

Despite always being incorrect, by 2018 it was most likely assumed the carefully laundered and spun public relations narrative for the last 50 plus years, only acknowledging limited harms had been skilfully and successfully established; and that this would continue to obscure the deeper picture indefinitely.

However events and situations personal to me, illustrated quite a different set of untold *Thalidomide* accounts. Both professionals and the public continue to be kept in the dark on the full extent of the cover up, and how even over 50 years on potential risks and hazard exist into the future, as the drug and its analogues are used in new ways.

Increasingly it became obvious lingering misinformation and propaganda needed to be finally challenged and overturned. By now valuable insights into the real accounts are increasingly becoming lost to history, though their legacy and potential for mistakes continues on into the future.

My personal journey at one level was simple and straight forward, but the many nuances revealed were profound, as they were deep and complex in the wider picture they uncovered. Every day events within my journey are interwoven with some savvy reportage, and endless ongoing background research. In total this has at least ascertained some of the unreported *Thalidomide* history to be pieced together, and enabled silent voices from within the womb and beyond the grave to have a voice and be heard.

An intriguing and revealing journey ahead...

"16 Weeks and Everything After..."© has turned negatives into positives, and opened doors and opportunities for others in more powerful positions to play their part in going forward.

"Dare to think differently
Dare to find answers others have not"

Paul 2017

PART I

The Conscious Informs the Subconscious

1

"Your Hands and Your Feet!"

Living and working in a half converted old apple loft is an arrangement that may sound idealistic. Perhaps in some ways it was, but it also had challenges like sharing with bats along with other occasional uninvited wild life, and the use of only one cold tap. The apple loft was a base and office for small scale conservation projects, where I lived and worked as a full time volunteer, combined with some part time jobbing work. There was also an Open University degree requiring only a handful of extra CAT points that kept being put off. In addition and of much greater importance, I made regular visits to share some time with my terminally ill mother. Throughout 2005 these occurred about every two to three weeks. My memories of these visits remain clear, and especially one occasion in particular.

Around late August 2005 I drove the usual 300 mile round trip to see her. The day felt like a double metaphor with a sense the seasons were about to change, and autumn was on its way. By the time I had completed the round trip, parked the car and climbed the steps up into the gloom of the Apple loft it was already dusk.

Still mulling over events of the day I part filled a kettle for a large mug of tea. In that moment of stillness waiting for it to boil, I felt a tangible connection with my mother. Emotional intelligence between her and I, was like a finely tuned sixth sense, and something I would not infrequently use to make her laugh. However on this occasion, the subject matter was distinctly more sobering and profound. Our shared emotional intelligence had been synchronised my whole life, but became most acute towards the end; and ensured this book would one day be written from little more than the directness of a look in only a handful of moments.

Silently her look and gentle nod said to me; *"Paul, if you can, go and deal with this for both of us"*. This same look had already been expressed to me before a number of other times, but on this instance earlier in the day my response to her had been different. Sensing her reduced health and increasing frailty, instead of only replying with a reciprocating look and nod, as I had done previously, this time I also gently said out aloud; *"OK Mum...don't worry,...I heard you...I got it!"*

With this my mother knew I would take things forward in future times, and somehow tackle the issues contained in this book. My hopes are it helped her find some form of closure and reduced a burden she had carried for about 40 years.

Around three years earlier in 2002, she had first informed me of the key facts, probably at a point for her when she sensed these were going to be her final times, regardless of not being certain how much of her time remained. As a precaution it was a good point to tie up loose ends and manage any outstanding business.

Without any prior warning my mother took hold of my hand and held it in hers. Instantly I knew something significant was up, as my hand had not been held in this way for about 30 years. The hand hold style was; *"be a good boy for your Mum"*. In the moment I was more than half expecting to hear my mother only had about 72 hours to live, or something very similar. The good news at that point was there were no such immediate prophecies, yet instead declarations more out of the ordinary than could have been imagined, and arrived at through a slightly farcical interaction.

To the best of my recollection in critical content the following account is in substance and nature verbatim correct. Although it was the case these sentiments, phrases and types of explanations were thereafter repeated to me on numerous occasions. Thus it's possible there may have been even more information at this first exchange, nonetheless the following is in essence 100% accurate;

"I took Thalidomide", my mother told me.

"Oh good, maybe it will help"? My initial reaction, said thinking of her prevailing cancer, and under the impression *Thalidomide* had, or might be used in some instances.

"No, not good", my mother replied.

"Might be? It's not had any time yet", I responded.

"No, not good...not good at all, thirty almost forty years ago", my mother added.

"How do you know? ...anyway you mean thirty to forty minutes ago. Expect it will take a day or two...before you see or feel any signs of it working..." I said as a comeback, as sensitively as I could.

"No...when I was pregnant with you", my mother persisted.

"So what...you're taking Thalidomide for the cancer though?" I said, half asking, and half confirming.

"No, I mean when I was pregnant with you", my mother again repeated, trying to convince me.

"So what's that got to do with anything? That was 30...40 years ago", I said softly, and in some confusion.

"I know...I took Thalidomide..." my mother calmly reinforced, in her usual measured and composed manner.

"It was called Distaval...*that was the brand...when I was*

pregnant with you…weeks 16 to 20", my mother added.

After a pause of silence my mother said, in a saddened and resigned way

"I took it (Distaval/ *Thalidomide) just with you…not your sister…no, not your brother…no not them…just you"*!

(Silence…that felt like a long time, but was probably not even half a minute)

The information was so out of context, there had been a bit of a time lag between me getting what was in fact being revealed, and realising it was not information relating to a form of cancer treatment. Yet in the silence and deep in my mother's eyes I caught her vulnerability of opening up to me. *"Please don't blame me, I didn't mean to, I didn't realise, I didn't know"*, the silence loudly informed me.

Looking back I made a kind and gentle nod of reassurance with my eyes, to let her know things were OK, and for her not to worry. Inside for me it wasn't exactly the entire case, but when something like this hits you blind side, there isn't time to assimilate it all. At that precise

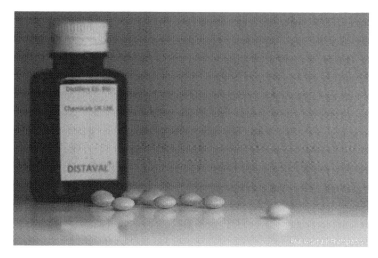

Distaval/ Thalidomide has a legacy of untold harms

point in time I was trying hard to prioritise what were the absolute most salient issues, and to do the right things as well as and above all not to do or say the wrong things.

Rejecting or blaming her was not ever going to happen, but I shall continue to stand by and up for her. Distaval/ *Thalidomide* should have been way beyond all reach in 1966; and regardless should not ever have been given to any woman who was or could be pregnant, whatever the year, including any years before or since. Even if she had gone to her G.P. and made a specific request for Distaval/ *Thalidomide*, then the G.P. should have declined. But instead my mother had visited her usual local G.P., because in her words, *"Morning sickness was going on forever"*.

When morning sickness is still continuing at weeks 16 of pregnancy, I expect it must feel like *"'forever"*, and it was the case she had a propensity to feel and suffer nausea. Even though she remembered her pregnancy with me gave her the worst and the most prolonged bout of morning sickness, of any of her pregnancies.

There were some more things my mother said to me after the initial *Thalidomide*/ Distaval disclosure, although I can't recall with enough precision to recount them verbatim.

Then she said, *"It didn't really affect you…well? …not that much…only a bit'…"* We both knew this was not the exact case or the entire situation, but I continued to show kind reassurance with my eyes.

Her second quote was as definitive as it was decisive and confirmed all that had remained unspoken, but by now was evident to both of us. Letting go of my hand my mother made the gesture of rubbing one hand over the other almost as if washing ones hands one at a time, and then pointed down with both index fingers, whilst at the same time linking left and right thumbs, and said to me *"Well...,"* – ***"Your Hands and Your Feet"***!

The implication was clear and left no room for misunderstanding because it referred to many situations during my childhood dating back 30 years and over. One example was aged eight soon after starting Cub Scouts my mother became a helper. Perhaps this was because of her concerns for me being so small, or maybe to stop potential mischief, but on reflection it was probably both. The strange thing was the situation arose from feet measuring comparisons with other boys. There was never any messing with my mother, probably due to some formative years spent in post war North Yorkshire. Immediately she came straight over and grabbed both of my hands, one in each of hers. Yet to my utter bewilderment and confusion, her repeated instruction, was to turn my hands over, then turn them back again, and wouldn't let go.

Even today I still recall how in a perplexed way saying to her, *"But we are comparing feet size, why are you looking at my hands?"* My mother let go of my hands and replied; ***"Your hands and your feet!"*** Something often repeated to me in a range of situations over future years, and even though not quite understanding what was implied, I always sensed it went deeper. Now these exact words and same precise gestures were being used relating to my exposure to Distaval/ *Thalidomide* at weeks 16 to 20 of her pregnancy. Their full meaning had finally become clear.

My gentle reply, *"Yes, I know, but don't worry; I've got used to my hands the way they are...and my feet. Anyway they have gone a long way ...and I have run and cycled more than most..., what are you worried about? You're not going to start worrying now...are you?!"* I said tongue in cheek, implying this is over 30 and nearer 40 years too late.

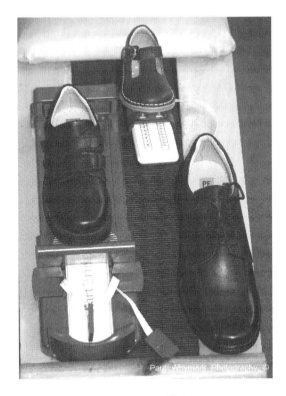

What is an 8 years old shoe size?
(Photography support: Bahoo Footware Malvern)

It made my mother smile, almost laugh. Today it brings
a sweet melancholy memory as it resurfaces again in my
book.

All the same to me it was abundantly clear she had
not stopped worrying about *Thalidomide* harms left in me
for nearly 40 years. Instantly I was aware of how she had
carried this burden, this significant unrevealed life event,
and how it had been continually with her. What had this
done to her? Over years and decades there had been
relentless ongoing reminders, for example; endless trips
to try and find shoes that might but invariably didn't fit my

feet, plus her many skilful adaptations to all my clothes over all the years.

My *"hands and feet"* are, and in particular were in childhood, the symbol and insinuation of my lack of height and stature. Concerns for my hands and feet had gone back to the time of being born. In more recent times I have come to think and suspect the Distaval/ *Thalidomide* she had taken caused her additional stress for the remaining time of her pregnancy; but by then it was too late and she was powerless. Clues to this are in how my father would express the extent and level of how she had worried about *"her baby"'* (me) during the pregnancy. Knowledge of the extent of her anxiety and of how it would have been sustained, no doubt provided an interesting set of dynamics between my parents, even before I was born.

On the first disclosure around 2002 I drove home at an optimum speed for saving the planet, nurturing fuel consumption by a light touch on the accelerator, in a tidy if not ageing 1.25 Ford Fiesta. Whilst burning no more petrol than was required my mind ran alight. Would a plain white World Wildlife Fund cardboard box, contain a red hard back book on Anatomy and Physiology, and if it wasn't there, where would it be?

On entering the house I didn't even stop to close the door, but simply ran up stairs to try and locate the file box. Despite not having referred to the Anatomy and Physiology text book for some time, I discovered it almost immediately where I hoped it might be. The book then fell open only one page away from the right place, as if somehow it already knew and was waiting for that very moment.

'Marieb (1992), Human Anatomy and Physiology, 2nd Edition', foetal development on p991, presented a relevant small typed sub box with a basic diagram of a 16 weeks

foetus [1]. Regardless of only being a rudimentary outline foetal sketch, it had uncanny similar visual proportions to me compared to diagrams for a foetus at weeks 21 to 30 and 30 to neonatal. In addition there were a few, but not many associated bullet points revealing how limbs and especially lower limbs are still developing. By implication this included hands and feet as all aspects continue to develop and grow to reach their final proportions during the relevant period of foetal development, weeks 16 to 20.

After that I can't remember, except the room was spinning, and I shut the book with a thud, continuing to sit on the floor in a bewildered state. It had been quite a day. So that was it, after all these years the reason for being less tall and reduced in height was down to Distaval/ *Thalidomide*. Deep in my subconscious and intuition I had always sensed and felt there was some reason lurking in the background, but up to the early 2000's I had always assumed the term *"Thalidomide"'* meant drastically reduced arms and legs or perhaps even none at all. As I have both of each I was somewhat of a contradiction; but then I hadn't previously known anything significant about the history of the drug. At school three to five years above my year there had been a small number of people who had suffered the stereotypical harm from pre-birth *Thalidomide* exposure. Yet that stereotype didn't reflect me, or my life.

There were a few other people labelled as *Thalidomide* nearer to my year, and even one who was in the same year as me. Yet they too didn't represent the typical stereotype i.e. without arms or legs, so called phocomelia, and referred to as *'flipper style'*. Any fellow school pupils labelled as *Thalidomide* I had only ever seen as a person and human being anyway and therefore hadn't really considered details of such impairments.

For all the new emerging perspectives, it was evident the subject was still highly sensitive and difficult to mention. The fact it had taken nearly 40 years for my mother to finally and unambiguously tell me what had made me the way I am, implies how much of a taboo subject this must have been. What were the dynamics between my parents concerning this taboo? Had there been a pact between them not to let on? Was it possible to not share this information even with all my childhood hospital trips to investigate my reduced stature? It was a sensitive subject requiring considerable further discretion and restraint on my part. Others have said my personal qualities and strength of character tend to lend themselves to such confidences and situations; perhaps ironic any such qualities have to a large extent been gained from my mother in the first place. Now the same woman suffering terminal illness had just made herself vulnerable, by addressing some incomplete business and tackling what for her had been an ongoing challenging issue carried for decades.

As usually is the case where a drug has harmed a baby during pregnancy, the mother is the person who carries the pain, and has to deal with additional day to day logistical difficulties.

This reality and context required support and reciprocation of courage, and I was not going to let her down by making it an issue, or even risking loading the smallest amount more on to her. It is my belief my mother knew and understood I did not and would not hold any blame towards her. It is very clear all accountability resides with the drug companies responsible, along with bio-symbiotic areas of the establishment. Who knows how much my mother carried all those years? As a mother what would that feel like?

There's a thought. Ask any mother and they would soon let you know.

However the feedback would be quite different to the spun and counterfeit presentations expressed thus far by the drug companies and bio-symbiotic corners of the establishment. Perhaps if anyone is still not sure of the burden a mother would carry, try raising the issue somewhere like BBC Radio 4 Woman's Hour or Mothers Net.

Now I knew my reduced stature was down to the drug Distaval, a brand of *Thalidomide*, taken during weeks 16 to 20 of pregnancy to help with morning sickness. Yet at the same time in many ways I didn't know that much. For a start how much smaller had this made me? Was this 1" or

'15 W. & E. A...' Photo - Art ©

Drawing of Margaret and Paul by Margaret's Sister Jennifer

1 foot? Had *Thalidomide* affected anything else in me, and if so what and to what extent? I sensed it was responsible for my dyslexia, shown to be profoundly evident during a recent assessment for the Open University. At the beginning of my personal journey these were strong hunches, but ones that would turn out to have intriguing revelations, and considered in much greater detail in future chapters.

Through shared emotional intelligence my mother repeatedly confirmed her belief in me to take on challenges in new ways, and to access an inherited deeper steely inner core. On occasions she would remind me of how I had undertaken a long sponsored walk, around a large country park and surrounding area of Leicestershire.

This was with cub scouts, but even before I had officially joined aged only 8 years and 10 days, yet no taller than a four year old. To finish the full distance meant having to run and march throughout the day to complete all the laps. However as an early indicator of my dyslexia all day I had thought the distance constituted 5 laps of 4 miles, but in fact required 4 laps of 5 miles. It wasn't until the arrival of dusk at the end of the day did the organisers realise my check cards showed the indisputable evidence of stamps and clips for all five separate circuits; with multiple check points lined up on each row, i.e. 5 sets x 5 miles, a total of 25 miles, a distance walked (and run) further than anybody else including young adults of 18 years old.

"It's not about finding your limits It's about finding what lies beyond them"

Anon

Classic 1970's bay window VW camper van

Rounding off the day, hot drinks and some sustenance got handed out from supporting camper vans and a mini bus, before being driven back home. Adults were in disbelief of my epic trek. Not long after the 3 day working week, economics meant negotiated settlements were arranged where 25 times expected sponsorship occurred. This was because sponsorship was quite generous per mile, assuming I would only do one maybe two miles at the most.

While at the Apple Loft during the late summer of 2005 I began to seriously consider the assignment ahead and the tenacity needed. Nonetheless I also sensed my mother was putting both her faith and trust in me to find a way to address the issues concerned, and in effect was her last gift to me.

Reflecting on countless events and situations from childhood and life that had gone before, my preliminary efforts had only made limited enquiry. Yet even by 2005 I sensed things may turn out to be less than straight forward. As it was clear a range of *Thalidomide* issues had been somewhat under reported, misreported or simply brushed under the carpet, leaving both professionals and the public ill informed in various ways. Although in 2005, I did not appreciate how slippery and evasive the subtle insidious nature of the 50 year cover-up had been. Nor did I realise it has left potential to inflict harms that currently would not even be attributed or picked up on in the future. But then I was unaware safety concerns continue for other drugs taken during pregnancy that also have lingering question marks and dubious transparency.

The journey that followed had numerous twists and turns, and started with little more than the clues from the simple phrase; *"Your Hands and Your Feet!"*

"The most difficult thing is the decision to act, the rest is merely tenacity" [2]

Emilia Earhart

2

Rebuilding Noah's Ark on a Coastal Footpath

During the first week of July 2005 the weather was some of the best that year. Dazzling sunshine was glinting in flashes off a deep blue sea, and above only the limits of a bright blue sky. During this week of sublime weather I was co-leading a group of fellow co-volunteers. We were working on a project in North East of England to repair and improve access along a coastal foot path on part of the Cleveland Way. Tasks included building boardwalk constructions out of wooden planks, nailed to what were referred to as stringers i.e. batten rail like pieces of wood. When the planks of wood are joined together they create a wooden frame structure that can be set flat to the ground, and used for constructing bridges and boardwalks.

In the shimmering heat around a dozen or so conservation volunteers were in a hive of activity, attaching the boards to the wooden rails. The industrious pursuit generated multiple rippling nailing sounds that bounced around the hot summer air, in a riotous and chaotic crescendo. As each nail was driven down snugly into the timber, it created a clamour of noise increasing then decreasing in tonal pitch; a sound like, the *'glug', 'glug', 'glug'* of water or liquid bouncing through a narrow necked glass bottle.

All week the sunshine had been like that of summers long lost, but then around the Thursday just after lunchtime the weather abruptly changed. Without warning

Sea rain then plan to build an ark

out of the blue there was a dramatic down pouring of rain. None of this mattered though as the rain was both warm, and provided an agreeable refreshing cooling effect in relation to the baking hot summer air. The huge rain drops, around the size of fifty pence pieces fell in a frenzy and produced a beautiful rainbow.

Surrounded by wooden boards being nailed together, it didn't take long before the predictable Noah's Ark repartee soon began. Perhaps it was the welcomed cooling effect of the down pouring of rain, but either way the light-hearted banter on predictions of the end of the world being nigh, soon became more philosophical. What would we actually need to build an Ark? Plus, how could we make an Ark in real life? Not that anyone was seriously suggesting Ark building, as an alternative afternoon activity.

One volunteer with good carpentry skills talked over some practicalities and logistics. He suggested how hard it would have been, and how '"we" (the modern western world), don't appreciate the skills and perseverance of peoples who built boats in traditional ways. Even building something as simple as coastal foot path steps, a boardwalk and bridge without electric tools, was hard enough. Plus the extra effort of having to carry everything required, form the mini-bus nearly a mile away, meant we could all appreciate old school boat building was a demanding process. We also knew facilities, (if not basic by 21st Century standards), were assured to clean and freshen up at the end of the day, plus a substantial evening meal was guaranteed. Building an Ark back in the day of Noah may not have been so straight forward in terms of living conditions either.

Discussions then took a twist and out of this came a startling revelation. One person stated, *"We have all the tools and the measuring devices Noah used"*. Looking around at the saws nails and hammers it was easy to see the sort of basic tools, albeit in a modern guise purchased from the local DIY centre.

"What about the measuring devices though?" Another co-volunteer asked.

"A cubit"; came the reply.

From years ago I knew the basic story of Noah and his legendary Ark, but couldn't quite recall what cubits were, so I asked, was it hand size? *"Well...partly"*, he answered. Adding, *"Cubits are the length of your lower arm"*, and expanded by explaining the difference between a full cubit, and a reach cubit. A full cubit is the measurement from the end of the middle and longest finger back to the tip of the elbow, with hand opened out and arm flat.

A reach cubit measurement is taken from the first set of knuckles, back to the tip of the elbow, and was described to me as; *"Imagine rowing a boat and holding onto an oar,*

*it's the distance from your hand wrapped around the end of
the oar back to the point of your elbow".*

[The word cubit comes from the Latin;, cubitõ, [1] v.
lie down, cubitum, 1, nt. elbow; forearm; cubit, cubo,
ui, itum, [1] v. lie down; lie asleep; recline at table [1].
Lying down and flat is tied to words like cube, a multiple
flat sided object that always lies down on one side. The
same again from recubo; to lie back, to recline: sub and
recumbo – recumbere – cubus, to lie back [2]. Out of this
derives recumbent, as in the form of a bicycle ridden from
a position of lying down.

Thinking about the explanation of the cubits, I came
back to him with a further question, *"But won't that vary
between sizes of different people?" "No",* he replied; then
clarified *"not between grown men anyway, as adult males
have cubits sizes about the same length, regardless of their
height".* Next he stated all the men present would have
around about the same cubit size, just like in Noah's day
when he built his Ark.

Minutes later being drenched by the largest spots of
warm rain a group of fully grown men, were lined up in
order of sequential cubit size. Adult males cubits size are
all much the same sort of dimensions. But my cubits and
reach cubits presented about 2½" (6.5cm) less than the
smallest cubit and about 4" (10cm) less than the largest of
the other men present on the day.

Perhaps not expected, but the tallest guys didn't always
have the longest cubits, as proportions between upper and
lower arm may vary within individuals, even though cubit
size is within a quite tight range. All the same every other
adult male present, except for me, were within the range;
c.18"–22" (46–56cm) for a full cubit, and 14½"-17½" (38–
44½ cm) for a reach cubit; as my future research would go

Paul Whymark Photography ©

Comparison of Paul's cubit to the minimum adult male cubit

onto show. My full Cubit however, is only 15½" (39cm) at over 2" (6cm) below the minimum – N.B. not the average, as is also the case for my reach Cubit at c.11¾" (29½ cm), i.e. over 2¼" (6cm+) less than the minimum [3].

The reach cubit is perhaps a more accurate assessment of limb proportions (ulna and radius bones between elbow and wrist), as hand lengths also varies within a range. Thus potential sub variables are excluded when only considering the ulna and radius bones of the lower arm. It may be that differentials of my full cubit and reach cubit suggest my hand size could be marginally increased by inherence of DNA for proportionally extra large hands, even though my hands are actually very small. This would be consistent with my grandfather on my mother's side, who had about the largest proportionally sized hands and feet I have ever seen on anybody whatever their height.

"If you don't expect the unexpected you will not find it, for it is not to be reached by search or trail" [4]

Heraclitus

Back in the moment of being drenched by the down pouring of warm rain observing the other guys cubit lengths, I simply knew my cubits were below levels of the absolute minimum size. Not that at this point in time I had ever researched cubit sizes before and didn't confirm this until quite sometime after. An unsettling feeling of Déjà Vous descended upon me, and I was instantly transported back in time to being 8 years old at cub scouts and the feet measuring comparisons. My feet were smaller than everyone else's, and 30 years later I now gained a new level of understanding from my mother's quote; *"Your Hands and Your Feet"!*

In some ways this event was the first of a number of real game changers, because it provided some definable level of certainty. It illustrates how my cubit lengths had been reduced by at least 2" (5cm), or perhaps 2½" (6.5cm) and maybe yet more. Either way this is smaller than not just the average, but the minimum amount for an adult male cubit by about 14.3% to 17.8%, and not in line with any per chance variation. Of course it may represent an even greater reduction resulting from Distaval/ *Thalidomide* exposure? For example, up to 3½" (9cm) of cubit length deficit equates to a 25% reduction of my arm development.

Using only a little lateral thinking it is a very good indicator of my overall height loss due to exposure of Distaval/ *Thalidomide*, knowing my feet and lower legs were also reduced, and by reciprocal proportions. Hence doubling my arm deficit [2 x [2½"(6.3cm)] = [5" (12.6cm)] equating to the deficit in my leg length and therefore height. This would put my real destined height to be at least around 5' 7" (170cm) in keeping with my grandfathers as I estimated. Yet if genetics destined my cubits to be more like the average (not just the minimum), then this means *Thalidomide* caused about a 25% reduction of my cubit length. Therefore equating to a reduction of 3½" (9cm), arm length and hence a reduction of 7" (18cm) of my leg length, which would have given me an overall height of 5' 9" (175cm); the same as my father's height. With a cubit of 17¼" (44.5cm) multiplied by 4 = persons height, as used in guides to human proportions, i.e. 5' 9" (175cm) [5].

In general it is often said, the population overall has become taller over the last 70 years, indicating if anything my growth was reduced beyond 14% and more like a 25%

Brilliant sewing by Margaret to adapt Paul's shirts for reduced cubit size

reduction. In shirt sizes I take a small adult male size, even though the arms need drastically turning up and trousers likewise. My mother would sew in brilliant sleeve tucks on the inside of all my shirts that were hardly noticeable from the outside. Typically the reduction was about 2½" to 4" (6.5cm to 10cm), but sometimes more.

Following cubit revelations on the coastal foot path I began to notice other male cubits and feet size. On rare occasions since when encountering other similarly compact sized adult males, I noticed they always have larger feet and hands than I do. Whilst living and working in Vietnam in 2012 and travelling daily through Hanoi on the bus, sometimes a similar sized or even a less tall adult male would stand alongside me and hold the roof handles for support. Upon which I would become aware his cubits were a bit larger than my cubits. This was regardless of South East Asian's in general tendency to be less tall than average western people, and may have slightly smaller proportions all round. However I didn't notice any other adult males with quite as small hands as me. It may be the case larger limbed races, such as males from some African heritages may have a propensity to have even marginally larger cubits.

Noah's Ark, in Genesis 6.15 [6], was said to have had dimensions of 300 by 50 by 30 cubits [one cubit was about 18 inches (45 cm)], and taken to imply the vessel was rectangular. See appendix for further cubit information. The word *"ark"* in Hebrew, *"teba"*, means, *"box"* or *"chest"* [7], and so perhaps the board walk and bridge construction made for the coastal footpath wasn't so different to Noah's Ark after all.

During the week working on the coastal foot path project, I sent my mother a picture postcard of the

Cleveland Way. Within only a few more days I visited her again, and we talked about improving access on the Coastal Footpath, shown on the postcard. Although I didn't mention any of the deeper meanings relating to building wooden board walks in the style of Noah's Ark. Not even when the expected moment came up, and my mother said, *"Did I tell you…I took* Distaval/ *Thalidomide weeks 16 to 20 when I was pregnant with you"*. This was her way of raising the subject, and so I quietly looked over at the innocuous postcard standing in full view, and with a gentle smile gave my standard reply, *"yeah…we talked about that"*, I said.

From this point on in midsummer 2005 my mother's health deteriorated yet further, and by late autumn her life was over. Since then there has been no way of going back to ask about more details; for example how I was born with a slight stork mark on my head, something not infrequently associated with *Thalidomide* babies. This is because the skull hadn't always fully developed and some extra skin in places creates a fold, even though in general it is grown out of. However one thing I will always wonder about, is whether doctors I saw in childhood hospital trips ever considered or advised that my cubit in childhood was so far off the norm?

This was very probable, but expects even the consultant didn't consider my cubit in relation to rebuilding Noah's Ark on a coastal footpath.

"I am not afraid of storms, For I am learning how to sail my ship" [8]

Louisa May Alcott

3

Growing Concerns

Following the disclosure of being impacted by Distaval/ *Thalidomide* between weeks 16 to 20 of my foetal development, I began reflecting on many aspects of my life that had gone before. Perhaps the most glaringly obvious would be better described, as concerns of not growing.

Looking back I now appreciate the *"Your Hands and Your Feet"* incident at cub scouts had caused my mother additional concerns and stress for my life ahead. Hence it acted as a catalyst for my attendance at biannual childhood growth clinics, from the mid 1970's to around the mid 1980's. The specialist doctor came up from a major London Children's Hospital to hold infrequent outpatient clinics in Leicestershire, and therefore we were considered lucky to be accepted to see him. The reason was supposedly to discover if they could make me any taller, but this never seemed plausible at the time, and much less so now. That said hormone replacement therapy was apparently considered at some length, with very circular discussions that never led anywhere; and just as well [1] because some cases of CJD (a variant of BSE) occurred due to such interventions.

In the mid 1970's besides the biannual outpatient attendance there was in addition an overnight stay for several days, although the precise reasons for which remained only partly undisclosed. A number of tests were conducted under partial and full anaesthetics. The order and perhaps the total range of tests are not entirely recalled today, as at the time I found them distressing.

My hands and feet came in for a lot more scrutiny, especially one afternoon when a crowd of various specialist doctors and nurses encircled me and deliberated at great length both my hands and both feet. But what were they looking for? Five toes on each foot, four fingers and one thumb on each hand. There was something quite perturbing by how these clever people might not be able to count from zero to five.

They decided on taking bone samples from my toes and fingers/thumbs. At the time this all felt quite troublesome and unnecessary. If they were worried about the size of my hands and feet why would they want to reduce the size, by taking away even more bone? Wearing a huge green operation gown the size of a tent feeling cold upset and like crying, but deliberately choosing not to, as I was transported to surgery. The biopsy must have taken no more than a needle scraping of bone because on coming around, much to my relief there were no observable differences; so it turned out they had left enough to be going on with after all.

What happened next was decidedly worse and the details are now somewhat vague as the memory has been partly blocked out, and because to a varying degree I was half sedated throughout the day. Nonetheless at least awake at the beginning I had to swallow a huge steel device a bit like a pebble attached to a long tube/ cord as it went down into my alimentary system. It was the largest thing I have ever swallowed and how many times the procedure was done I'm not sure, but it wasn't pleasant. X-rays were required for guiding the device during the procedure something I still remember seeing on a green TV screen lying on my side feeling very sick. The biopsy was for analysis and assessment of samples of what had been eaten and samples of my intestine, to try and ascertain any reason for not digesting food, and therefore not growing. It was a long procedure over the day, and then I remained in hospital for one or two more nights while other tests were made. Yet more blood tests were taken, how much blood did they want? Were they cooking with it?

Following the above, hospital visits returned to biannual events that seemed boring and like a complete waste of time, as somehow I knew I wasn't going to be any taller. Mandatory blood tests were always taken. Tedious detailed repetitive measuring would be made for limb proportions; in particular my lower legs and lower arms, along with extensive hand and feet size measuring. Deliberation followed with the use of charts, showing potential pencilled projected growth increases.

Great concern for my hands and feet continually came up with the specialist doctor. He would studiously look at and examine my hands for minutes at a time before strangely adding something like; *"There's nothing missing...but a bit on the small side that's all"*. Only six months later he would repeat exactly the same process, and mysteriously come to the same blatantly obvious conclusion. My feet similarly got the same level of examination, and were unconventionally praised in equal measure for what seemed to me to be so unbelievably evident, i.e. they were all there.

Other examinations included using bright lights to peer into my eyes and ears, plus ear audio tests, reading tests, x-rays examinations of lower legs, feet, hands and lower arms, and in fact all over from head to toe.

A chat with the doctor would follow where he would reassure me very sympathetically everything was all right, and not to worry. After this my mother would have a considerably longer private consultation e.g. half an hour or more, while I was made to wait outside. What else was there to talk about? We had just agreed everything was all right. In the corridor I would sit without complaining, but get extremely bored.

In June 1976, the year the UK suffered a serve drought, we sat outside in the corridor waiting our turn in the queue. The overnight stays with the unpleasant and invasive tests afore described were still very prominent in my mind. Hence I did not want to go back to hospital, afraid of what they might do to me next. Being very reasonable and grown up I started a discussion with my mother requesting not to ever visit to the hospital again. Unable to gain agreement it defaulted to pestering her about leaving before we had even seen the doctor. As a result, my mother asserted, *"We are visiting the hospital to see if they can make you taller"*. My reply was, *"but I don't want to be bigger, and I am quite happy as things are, now can we go home please?!"*

With the spiralling discussion continuing, my mother said to me, *"Maybe they will find a way of making you taller, maybe they will have some medicine to make you bigger"*. My reply was to ask, *"Why would they want to do that?"* Long before the term Freudian slip was in my vocabulary, I somehow knew what followed next was more than a simple a mistake. In exasperation my mother replied; *"In case you took some medicine that made you smaller."* At first I was lost for words; but not for long, and I pursued this line, insisting in complete confusion; *"But I haven't ever taken any medicine to make me smaller"*? By now my mother was very self-conscious and embarrassed at a level that seemed entirely disproportionate, but continued to try to tell me *"No, **you** didn't take any medicine that made you smaller"*. The reality was something was out of sync and out of place, and in a significant way, but what?

Then as now her denials of me taking medicine that made me smaller never felt quite right. At the time my continuing response was, *"I'm never taking Tixylix (children's cough medicine) ever again"*. There was nothing else besides cough medicine I knew I had ever taken. Except travel tablets, but they only made a person drowsy; didn't they? Anyway my siblings and cousins had all taken travel tablets and they weren't small. Nonetheless I wasn't certain the possibility could be entirely ruled out. What about an antibiotic? That was more difficult to be sure, but I believed other people had taken them and they weren't small. Anyhow I wasn't convinced I had ever taken an antibiotic? Just in case I decided never to take Tixylix again, unless of course it could be proven not to make me smaller, and as a precaution all future travel tablets from then on would be hidden and not taken.

But what could it be? These thoughts ran around my head for the next decade and a half, into the 1990's. By my late twenties, early thirties gradually such sentiments drifted off, and eventually I stopped thinking about them.

At the end of a visit in December 1978 I had to sit outside in the corridor. My mother continued a particularly long discussion with the consultant, until suddenly she appeared out of the consulting room looking unexpectedly very angry in a quiet but deep intense fury. Striding straight past me at pace she was soon half way along the corridor. I ran after her, but was only unsure of how to handle the situation on catching her up. Her usual calm manner and light complexion now expressed an enraged totally furious look. Somehow I knew it had to be something to do with the reason for me being small, so I asked, *"have they told you why"?* My mother said nothing, and carried striding down the corridor. The fake fur liner on her winter coat again confirms it was December, and partly concealed her body language, but not enough for me not to realise and sense there was something very wrong. As we had just been to see a doctor for reasons of why I was small it seemed obvious it must be related to this. Notwithstanding asking again it was made very clear to me there was to be no nonsense. Under the circumstances I was very quiet on the subdued drive home, even though I knew she wasn't cross or angry with me, or I was in any sort of trouble. For such a non-event it had considerable additional meaning because for my mother this was completely out of character and because it represented something of a lioness defending her cub. Despite being only around twelve years old and not able to articulate such things I somehow knew it, and now refer to it as "quiet maternal fury".

The following June, 1979, warm sunlight poured into a large airy hospital consultancy room, through half closed metal blinds. It didn't seem unusual, or an infrequent occurrence to have a lower arm/ hand or lower leg/ foot x-ray, but I only recall one skull x-ray, taken laterally when I was twelve years and ten months old. It was projected onto a large white screen on the wall. The doctor and my mother talked about the image of my skull, but why were they looking at it for my size? My questions persisted to the point where the doctor told me, *"We are looking at your skull x-ray to see if your head developed in pregnancy"*. At the time it seemed like a joke. Of course my head developed during pregnancy otherwise I wouldn't have a head, and anyway why wait around twelve years before checking that one out? It felt so unbelievable I requested a different explanation. Although I was told it was just to check everything was OK, but somehow it didn't feel like the whole answer.

Another insight from my childhood hospital visits arose from a consultation with the specialist doctor in childhood growth. It may have been as late as June 1981, but my hunch is June 1980. My mother was sat to my left, and the doctor at an angle to my right. They were discussing something but trying to do so without saying the actual words, so making *'umm'* and *'err'* noises. No longer able to follow the drift of the consultant and loosing the thread of the incomplete speech, my mother said, *"So he is then?"* The doctor replied, *"Bilateral"*. In some surprise my mother responded, *"Oh, so then he isn't?!"*… But the doctor answered *"No, he is"*. My mother replied, *"But so you mean he isn't"*. By now there was so much confusion arising from the double negative's stacking up on top of one another. The doctor said, *"He is bilateral, not unilateral"*. To which my mother confirmed, *"Oh, so he is then?!?"* The doctor replied something like *"Yes, and so yes he is"*. Over many previous sessions and years I had picked up on a lot of undertone subtext funny speak, but this was just crazy and so I pursued it with them, *"What do you mean bilateral or unilateral, what does that mean anyway? …And what's it all about?"* The answer I got was equally mad, but it was the best that could be got out of either of them. *"Bilateral means we are checking you have two arms and two legs, and you do, so it is all OK"*.

My thoughts were, all this for deciphering I have two arms and legs, when it is so obvious? Yeah right! The terms bilateral and unilateral had no doubt been mentioned prior to this incident but that particular one sticks in my mind, as by this point in time I was becoming too old and insightful to be fooled by adults talking over the top of me. It was all very strange and confusing; yet again I sensed there was something to do with why I was not taller being withheld from me, but what? Visiting a doctor for around seven years to determine if I had two arms and two legs when it was and is so obvious didn't add up.

The hospital events above are today obviously all various *Thalidomide* leads the consultant and his colleagues were finding and reviewing. My hunch is he did his best and tried to look on the positive side, knowing there was nothing he could do to counter the drug companies and establishment propaganda that played down the extent of harm *Thalidomide* could cause, along with the wider scale of the issue. Even by 2005 before the end of my mother's life, I knew and understood all the hospital trips added to the burden she had carried due to the misinformation about the drug; before, during and after she was given Distaval/ *Thalidomide* in her pregnancy with me.

"A little inaccuracy saves a ton of explanation" [2]

Saki 1870-1916

Since the early 2000's other but related concerns became evident. For a long time I was unsure of how much my other relatives knew that I had been affected by Distaval/ *Thalidomide*. In the summer of 2005 a conversation between my parents took place when I was present, leaving me with the impression my father knew at least

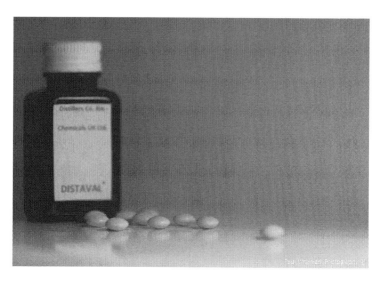

Deeper untold meanings of Distaval/ Thalidomdie at weeks 16 to 20

a limited amount. They had deliberated the name of the doctor who administered a jab to counter Rubella by increasing immunity, and then only a few weeks later prescribed Distaval/ *Thalidomide*. My mother thought this same doctor's name was *"Gordon"* based on initials of Dr G. Fr. Nonetheless she went on to agree the name *"George"* when my father made a joke out of it saying *"By George it was him"*. Although my father thought the doctor they had seen together for the Rubella jab was called Dr H., even though he could not recall his first name. My mother stated it was the same person but thought he was called Dr G Fr., but my father thought Dr G Fr had already retired by then (1966). Nonetheless both my parents agreed the doctor concerned was quite tall compared to the other doctors, plus he was the *"Young one"* due to a significant age gap between him and his colleagues, even though they continued to differ on the doctor's name.

They were referring to the same person that was clear, thus if nothing else at least I knew the doctor concerned was *"quite tall"* and the *"Young one"* in 1966. In addition I knew the same doctor had been seen for a preventative measure against *Rubella* only a few weeks earlier, and he went on to prescribe Distaval/ *Thalidomide* at the beginning of March 1966.

Around two years after my mother's passing I tried to find out more from my father, but he was still really struggling to come to terms with losing my mother. More challenging was how his aging years had significantly reduced his memory. In addition I had long suspected my father had some form of aspersers, not least due to how he would not get the obvious from situations like the above. Hence his lack of any recollection since has left me wondering how much of the situation he previously really understood or appreciated. It turned out none of my aunties or an uncle on my mother's side had been aware either. This came as a bit of a surprise, but much less so that my younger siblings knew nothing. By then I realised the taboo had been greater than I had previously thought, and it began to dawn on me going forward would be a solo assignment.

Between 2004 and 2008 I had worked relentlessly hard and juggled life, to get into a position of being able to undertake a humble small scale project managed self build house. It was the only way to get around ever growing impossible economics for people not on mega bucks, and not with secure guaranteed work, but with only one lifetime to pay for everything. Despite living extremely modestly for years, wider macroeconomic events unfolded to create unworkable dilemmas, and in this context I had to put on hold both self build plans and further endeavour on the Distaval/*Thalidomide* trail.

Any progress during this time was made more by serendipity than anything specifically planned or thought out. For example, around 2006 to 2007 I was in conversation with a couple of off duty doctors. One noted my ear-to-eye line ratio is not how it is for everyone else, i.e. I have a small but notable drop of about a ¾" (2cm). In itself this is no big deal. Despite previously knowing nothing about foetal ear positions, I instantly realised it related to Distaval/*Thalidomide* exposure at weeks 16 to 20 of foetal development. The off duty doctors were remarkably arrogant and inflexible in their denial of the even the possibility, and I quickly let the subject drop. It provided my first real insight and lesson as to how much in a silo some (but importantly not all) in the medical professions/ institutions can be; i.e. naive and easily duped by drug companies airbrushed historical accounts. All the same my perception on my ear position did turn out to be correct [3, p9-p14, p90-p92], and would later have much greater significance to be covered in future chapters. Since then it has become evident it is not only the position of my ears, but also the angle illustrating subtleties of how I was freeze framed at the 16 week stage of foetal development.

In the course of working on this book I have heard personal accounts of other people being given Distaval/ *Thalidomide* in pregnancy in the UK, around the mid 1960's. Some reports were from a little earlier, around 1962, 1963 and 1964, while others just after in 1965, 1966, 1967 and 1968, with one even as late as around 1980; indicating active use of *Thalidomide* continued at some level for years longer than might be supposed.

These accounts would be given to me at unexpected times and places. Two occurred within half an hour in 2013 on visiting a well known local sculptor, Guy Woodford to research body ratios and ear-to-eye-lines. On outlining my situation he told me of how his wife in the early 1960's, Pauline, had been given Distaval/ *Thalidomide* during her pregnancy. He praised in retrospect her intuition that somehow picked up the drug had a bad vibe, even though confessing at the time he had thought there would be no problem from something so seemingly innocuous. As a result of Pauline's savvy insight she did not take Distaval/ *Thalidomide* and had a healthy baby girl, Tamsin, during a time when the drug was entering its highest use during 1961, and was being given out like candy. The conversation had been interesting and Guy, who had been both sculpting and tutoring for many years, shared with me his sound appreciation of human anatomical proportions and ratios. For example how a person's height will be 10 times hand size, plus how cubits represent ¼ of a person's height. His knowledge was really informative and he helpfully suggested there might be a book that would be of further interest, ironically published in 1965 to 1966.

We went to another class room where an art tutor was preparing for her afternoon class. Guy enquired if a book he had in mind was present, and would it be OK if we took a quick look at it. She asked why, and I made a very superficial explanation, pointing out my own ear-to-eye line ratio. In a further twist she then informed me of being given Distaval/*Thalidomide* during her pregnancy of 1965 to 1966. Like Pauline three years earlier, she too didn't take the drug, but only due to unexpectedly feeling better on arriving back home.

Her Distaval/*Thalidomide* prescription around July 1965 is even more perturbing, as its intended use was for during early stages of pregnancy, revealing the case in point; i.e. no acknowledgement of any risks even in the first trimester of pregnancy had ever satisfactorily been made, let alone reliably communicated by governments or drug companies post "withdrawal" from the wholesaler. The art tutor's and my mother's situation illustrate how this was happening right across the UK, in the mid 1960's three to four years after the supposed "withdrawal" from the wholesaler.

Since then I have learnt of more people who were harmed by *Thalidomide,* but who are also not on any official figures, because they had unilateral harms, and these didn't fit retrospective stereo type recognised criteria. In this context it was not only possible, but inevitable some pregnant women were put at risk from *Thalidomide* in 1966, at or after weeks 12 of pregnancy and quite probably earlier. It transpires elsewhere in the world around 1965 other brands of *Thalidomide* continued to be openly used. In Spain *Thalidomide* consumption during pregnancy went on for years and well over a decade latter [4, see series]; and even over 20 years after it was supposedly withdrawn from the wholesaler in Germany. This resulted in *Thalidomide* harms in Spain being inflicted on the unborn in the mid 1980's [5]. Italy too had reported continued *Thalidomide* use in the mid 1960's, along with other countries ranging from Brazil to Belgium.

For years after 1962 when *Thalidomide* began "withdrawal" from the wholesale market, the drug was much more available and used than might be implied by retrospective P.R. spun miss-presentation. Michael Magazanik of the legal team Slater Gordon in Australia, who fought for Lyn Rowe in 2012, and who wrote an excellent book on the case in 2015 called *"Silent Shock"* [6], informed me of an extract from; History of *Thalidomide* Embryopathy, p205. Here it is evident further recognised cases did occur way beyond 1962. In Germany alone at least 81 new cases were recorded between August 1962 and 1967 [7]. In addition it is essential to appreciate these are not the full number of people harmed, but only a limited number. This is because the figures were based on the misperceptions of *Thalidomide* harm, by using inaccurate underestimating accounting processes; to be fully explained and expanded on further in future chapters.

The era of August 1962 to 1967 covered a time from 4 years prior to my birth to one year after. The Grünenthal Company, owner and manufacture of *Thalidomide*, had made no more than only a begrudging "withdrawal" from the wholesale market of Contergan/ *Thalidomide*, on the 27th November 1961 [8, p103-p104]. This was not a complete ban, and much less a satisfactory complete global recall. What it implied was more about a withdrawal of new supplies entering the market, but said little about existing stocks that by then probably amounted to tens, if not hundreds of millions of tablets globally.

Reflecting back on many aspects of my life and on a continuing personal journey since the early 2000's I learnt of a wide range of issues, and indirect issues that got brushed under the carpet. No documentation for the tens of millions if not more tablets left out in society, has ever been forthcoming in my research. But then on exploration at the Dista Products Archive no absolute numbers were forthcoming for how many tablets had been produced and sold. Without knowing reliable numbers that went out, it clearly was not going to be possible for a full satisfactory national and or international recall. This goes part way to explain some of the various accounts I have heard of over the years of what happened to the large amounts of remaining stocks post "withdrawal" from the wholesale market. One for example was said to be for use in N.H.S.

dental practice as a pre-treatment calming tablet. In these situations where the drug was given to a woman who could or might have been pregnant, it is highly unlikely any assessment whether she was pregnancy or not, or what stage her pregnancy was at would have been made. How today would it be known any impairments or medical complications in babies that will have lasted a life time were as a result of a trip to the dentist? Especially as many of the harms and consequences are still not acknowledged or recognised by medics even today in 2018.

Increasingly I have sensed *Thalidomide* was most likely not the only drug to have similar issues that received a spun P.R. rinse, and then became obscured over successive decades. A process of denial, distorting, and distracting has enabled drug companies and governments to be let off the hook, by simply waiting for people who were harmed to quietly come the end of their lives.

In contemporary times we can only learn from the past if universal transparency is made in all sectors and all areas concerned, and at the present time we do not have this. As a result the legacy of deference in medical and government institutions continues to have growing concerns.

'I hear and forget, I see and remember. I do and I understand' [9]

Confucius (551 – 479 B.C.)

PART II

Deeper Realisations

4

In the Deep End and
Tri-ing new things

Aged ten in the final year of junior school I went to a swimming pool for the first time. It was an echoing 1960's prefab concrete building at the University, with a somewhat overpowering chlorine disinfectant. Although only a shallow depth the water came up to and above my chin, when I was standing on absolute tip toe, and then bobbing off the base of the pool. The depth of the water between opposing ends of the pool only 15m apart, varied by no more than about ½" to 1" (1.25cm to 2.54cm), but this was enough for me to become out of my depth. Being a non-swimmer at the time it led to apprehension as to which end of the pool the teacher would put me in. Not all teachers were so believing or interested, and thus this would necessitate arguing the situation all over again from session to session.

Towards the end of the final year of Junior's just before heading off to high school aged almost 11 years old I learnt to swim at a basic level. This was enough to achieve a 10m badge. My mother had real concerns of my lack of swimming ability, and to boost confidence she would take me swimming throughout the summer holidays, and then got me on to swimming lessons. More examples of how as a mother she had worried concerning subtle indirect consequences of Distaval/ *Thalidomide* life reducing potential. On being lent a pair of swimming goggles my mother saw this would provide the confidence

Unimpeded vision assists wider learning

needed and soon got me a pair, and my swimming rapidly improved.

Stinging eyes became no more and instantly provided unimpeded vision, opening up a whole new world. Overnight teachers, who had previously been trying to get me in the deep end, could no longer get me out. In a short time I gained a reasonable standard of swimming and within a couple of years achieved a 10Km swim. In later times I went on to teach swimming, often to older adults, but whatever the age of the person I always remembered how it felt being a non swimmer.

"Don't limit your challenges, Challenge your limits"

Anon

From being a teenager until my early thirties despite being of small stature, I had a go at a range of multisport activities based around swimming, cycling, and running. Duathlons tended to be considered as run–bike–run, but could be swim–run–swims. Other variants were not unheard of. Biathlons had only two events such as swim and run, or run and bike, and in general multisport activities didn't have predictable distances or consistency of format. Perhaps people who didn't participate in such off the wall pastimes in the 1980's and early 1990's, would no more have heard of them than triathlons. The latter is now an Olympic event with a standard format, aptly known as Olympic or Standard Distances; 1.5 Km swim, 40 Km cycle and 10 Km run, surrounded by significant sponsorship and media following.

Prior to standardization the events calendar was as eclectic and eccentric as the combinations of distance, and perhaps the participants. Mini-triathlons emerged termed as sprint format, and typically these had lesser distances than the now standard Olympic distance. Drafting, (slip streaming behind another rider) in the bike phase was prohibited, and sometimes enforced with motorcycle intervention and penalty points, to ensure only time trialling i.e. rider against the clock.

Many tri-athletes and multi-sport partakers were often specialists or past masters in one specific discipline. Somewhere in the mid 1980's I first heard of multi-sports and triathlon with its links back to a surfer culture ethos of the 1960's, and '70's in California. Athletes such as Scott Minolina, Scott Tinley and Dave Scott undertook super human feats on a daily basis, later pursued by an ultra league led by Mark Allen, plus a new level of participants at shorter distances. During early times multisport athletes gaining a podium position would often get no more than a hand shake, but on occasion possibly extended to something like a couple of beers. However lifestyle sports were more about participation in new challenges, together with other kindred sporting counter culture spirits. It offered a more radical, daring and emboldened existence, seeming ever more at odds to where everything else in life appeared to be headed.

During the 1980's significant industrial changes took place in the East Midlands making it seem a long way from the life style sports of California. It was a lot less sunny, the rain was much colder and there was no coastline to go surfing on; even if the fossil Charnia showed this hadn't always been the case hundreds of millions of years earlier [1]. Yet perhaps there was something of a closer ethos between warm Southern California and the Loughborough area, although it could be hard to fully quantify.

Loughborough was a student town with a P.E. teacher training college, and a reputation for sporting excellence, with such lifestyle leanings long before it became a wider social norm. Even in the early 1980's at any time of day or night, and on any day of the year at least one person would be out running. Today this might not sound like anything so unusual, but at the time it was notably unlike most places in the UK, and provided a sub-culture of greater acceptance to sporting open-mindedness. During the summers, residential blocks and quarters of the University often resonated to mid Atlantic sounds of Fleetwood Mac in a way that sort of implied a de facto Californian connection.

Around the mid 1980's I would sometimes see one individual who was an exceptionally good athlete. On occasions he would appear not far in front of me, while on my daily run along Forest Road, or around an adjacent Field (exactly 1Km around the parameter, but probably now all built on). With some mild exuberance of youth, sometimes I would try to close the gap a bit on this guy. Yet no matter how gradual, or much effort I expended, he would always comfortably match or more than match with ease any of my increases in pace, keeping his distance ahead or even pulling further away. It was frustrating but understandable, as was to be discovered on watching the men's 5000 final of the 1986 European championships. Here the same guy Jack Buckner won Gold. It was a great race and won at a fast championship pace in an exceedingly strong field; including Tim Hutchings and Steve Ovett from the UK, plus a depth of top international stars. Jack Buckner's European Games winning time of 13 minutes 10 and 15/100th seconds has continued to stand as an impressive championship record some thirty years on [2].

The name Jack Buckner as a top runner was already well known to me, but somehow I hadn't realised he was the same person at times appearing in front of me on my daily run. It was clear he was in a much higher league of elite runners' way above my level. Back on planet earth as an average club runner, I took part in road and cross country activities. Generally fellow runners of a similar level, but who were also considerably taller than me, would not infrequently comment on my stride ratio. Notably they took about 3 strides, for about every 5 strides I made whilst running at the same speed; something repeatedly pointed out to me over many years by different people in different places.

Out of curiosity I calculated how much quicker I would be able to run if I had greater leg length. It was long before carbon blade limb extensions, and no more than a pointless hypothetical academic ponder. Calculations were based on maintaining the same cyclic stride rate, but with an enlarged stride from 1m (my actual stride) to 1.15m gained by a 4" to 5" (10cm to 12.5cm) longer leg length (like my grandfathers). Appling some maths reduces the number of strides required to cover the same distance, and thereby reduces times as the finish would be arrived at sooner. It can be calculated using the reciprocal i.e. = 100cm divided by 115cm = 0.87 to 2 d. p. Multiplying the old number of strides by 0.87 gives the hypothetical imaginary new reduced number of strides required to cover the same distance. Translating this hypothetical situation using the formula; time = distance/ speed reduces both effort and stride numbers to match peers, or to enable an increase in speed to have joined athletes at higher levels. All the same it's unlikely anybody in 1986 was going to keep up with Jack Buckner, not even with 50cm carbon leg extensions.

"Tri-athlete, n; "A person who doesn't understand one sport is enough"

Anon

Beyond philosophical consideration of any hypothetical potential, tri-sport and multi activities offered both gains of wider character building, and unexpected discoveries of self awareness. Cycling in particular provided some pertinent insights.

Spinning refers to turning over smooth pedalling revolutions with fluidity, enabling efficient utilization of leg power. A cadence range around 93 to 118 RPM was my optimum spinning zone regardless of gear size. In any gear extra leverage is good as it harnesses power, but only so long as it doesn't prevent spinning. An over long crank reduces ability to spin due to creating a lumpy effect that's inefficient and causes injury.

Over many years there was an ongoing contradiction as to the length of crank that in theory should provide my ideal leverage/ spinning combination. Text books recommend a crank length of 160mm or 162.5mm, for someone of my height and leg length. I tried these plus 165mm, and also 167.5mm, but found none of them as effective as 170mm. For anyone not so familiar with nuances of such cycling technicalities, a 10mm crank length increase is a huge difference. Most people would have a real dilemma in making a 2.5mm jump of additional leverage [i.e. 160mm to a 162.5mm, or 170mm to a 172.5mm]. Had my legs been 4, 5, 6, or even 7 inches longer, then clearly an even greater crank length would have been turned. For example; 175mm and perhaps even up to 180mm, again resulting in improved speed and performance.

The reason why I could turn over a much higher gear than would be expected for my height came to light when measuring up for a custom steel bike frame. It was observed my upper leg has a longer proportional ratio to lower leg than would normally be expected for males. This also explains why in football I could produce a power shot more than might be anticipated, from someone of my height. No surprise these same proportions are reciprocated in my arms (i.e. cubits), and elucidate as to why my handle bar reach set up has over the years resulted in some novel arrangements.

The self reflections so far have concerned the more overt obvious physical observations than the final discovery. Around 1990 top cyclists and tri-athletes began

Paul Whymark Photography ©

Bicycle racing offered deeper understandings than could have been imagined

using sunglasses/ rap around eye shields, providing protection from insects etc; something that makes a lot of sense if cycling downhill at 40 mph. At the end of the 1980's early 1990's more lens colour options were becoming available. On trying on a pair of Oakley Half Razors it left me aware of a real discovery. It wasn't the blue frame or grey/white arms with a squidgy grip nose piece, but the lens they came with. Quite a deep orange hue described as *"Rust"*. It made an unexpected but notable difference to my vision, and yet without any magnification. For example when I look at a tree the branches become visible, but disappear into a morphed mass when the orange lens are not worn, and this is the case for many other things also.

On the surface it was a bit of a contradiction, as I had believed my eyesight was otherwise quite good, i.e. I could read the letter charts with single characters and big gaps right down to the smallest sizes. Something I demonstrated in tests from infant school onwards, and during regular hospital visits throughout childhood. Letter size clearly didn't explain the improvements of the orange lens; however the reduces glare and colour contrast significantly improveing my visual acuity. Sharing this with other people, I would encourage them to try the orange lenses and experience these benefits first hand. However their responses didn't ever quite give me the impression it improved vision for them as much as it did for me. Use of light orange lenses made the whole world sharper and easier to see. Plus it makes the world sunnier, and quickly became essential for being outside on or off the bike, gaining a one liner of, *"better than drugs and without the side effects"* ©. The greater and more profound significance of this finding is revealed in the next two chapters.

In previous times I was oblivious to the possibility my height, limb proportions and total length, together with vision deficit idiosyncrasies had any underlying connection. However on learning of my exposure to Distaval/ *Thalidomide* at 16 to 20 weeks of foetal development these and many other things all became seen in a very different light, and understood on quite different terms. Before such awareness in earlier times of my multisport escapades and adventures, the only focus was going for the deep end and Tri-ing new things.

"Above all, train hard, eat light, and avoid (TV and) people with negative attitudes" [3]

Scott Tinley
(1980's Pioneering World Class Tri-athlete)

5

Dairy or Diary?

From the earliest of my school days as a first year Infant, reading and writing didn't make much sense. It only seemed strange and complicated. Numbers and sums were a bit more understandable but drawing and making things were by far the best option. Not much had changed a year later on entering second year infant classes, and by then I had the sinking feeling and sense of falling further behind. During this year I was given some extra hearing tests, plus also visual tests using the chart with decreasing letter size and increasing gaps size, yet these didn't reveal any apparent issues.

My junior classes started with a joint class of 7 to 8 year olds, and were on the same school site as the Infants, but with an increased allocation of school field. The junior class teacher was Miss C., a kind and gentle person much liked by everybody. I was one of a minority of children who were taken out of the main class for remedial reading and teaching. My reading was not good and I was unable to read much at all, despite being otherwise quite communicative. The remedial reading class had a bit of a stigma, as it implied thick and useless, even though this was not the intention. The remedial teacher meant well and no doubt did her best, but how much these classes helped my reading remains uncertain. Whilst with Miss C. and not out at remedial English lessons I had mixed results. When there was a topic to choose from that I could make more sense of, then perhaps I achieved a nominal satisfactory standard. Nonetheless English comprehension was beyond vexing and I had no idea what they were really on about, coming last in the class every time.

In art things I managed to draw a circular tin in 3D and get a reasonable mark, perhaps like football it indicated some spatial awareness. Maths classes included, Bases, i.e. base 10/ metric, base 5, base 7, base 2 binary, etc., and in this I achieved some of the top marks as well as being one of the first to finish. In class work more generally I would finish last, and usually not get much right, so how that happened was a bit of a mystery.

By September 1975 to June 1976 I moved to a new class for the third year juniors, with a new teacher I didn't make a good connection with. Looking back these were different times, and one never knows what issues her life was encountering. Even only aged nine years old there was always something that made me sense her life might not be a happy one, if so I wish her well and hope things got better.

In that year only two things are remembered. The first was being accused of pinching a reading book from the library, even though this was not the case. The second thing etched onto my memory is the reading and spelling tests held in front of the class. One in particular stands out, with the word in question being diary or dairy? I couldn't have told you then, let alone now, and all I recall is being asked to spell it out aloud letter by letter. Of course getting the letter sequence order the wrong way around perhaps did look like insolence or bad behaviour, even though this was not the case. Punishment was swift and implemented with a steel biro each time I got it wrong.

Over the year there were enough spelling tests to go wrong, and this only made me freeze and get more

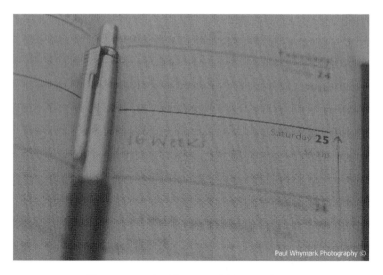

The greater significance of diary or dairy

stressed, and as a result my spelling deteriorated. It was hard to imagine my spelling could be any worse, but I expect you get the general point. Even 40 years later without spell check, my spelling is doomed to failure. This is despite having a considerable verbal lexicon enabling an otherwise articulate and expressive vocabulary. Today computers have spelling corrections, even if the American version of English in the 2000's A.D.P.M. (Anis Dominie Post Microsoft) adds another level of confusion for UK English. Nonetheless the American version is more often than not going to be closer to being correct than my own attempts. At the same time, English is an ever more global language and a hybrid that continues to evolve.

Being no good at reading why would I want to pinch a reading book from the library? At 9 years old the only things I wanted to do were to play football, climb trees, ride a bike, do some drawing or build another model Aeroplane kit.

"I have decided to keep a full Journal (diary), in the hope that my life will perhaps seem more interesting when it is written down" [1]

Sue Townsend (as Adrian Mole)

Simply starting out at high school at age 11 was enough, in particular because the boys were all a lot bigger than me, and some were already the height of an adult. To add to this, autumn 1977 caught fault lines of two cultural eras, pre-punk and post-punk, making it as is sometimes said particularly interesting times. Both were survived by resilience and some savvy wit. Three years later in the last term there was a physics exam.

The class was a mid stream average set. My position was perhaps mid to upper level, not always the absolute best but reasonable, and every so often I would have a good day around the top. The physics teacher, Mr D., was a former WW2 airman who flew in Lancaster's mostly on reconnaissance operations as the camera man at the back of the plane. A position sometimes referred to as tail end Charlie's, something statistically he probably was unlikely to have survived. Mr D. was a likeable teacher in many ways, although he was a long time believer in corporal punishment.

Mr D., read out the final year test results in reverse order, i.e. lowest to highest. *"ZERO"* marks, he called out, and a brief pause followed my name. A considerable punishment seemed imminent and I thought I was going to pass out. This was regardless of three years of impeccable behaviour and being seen as a good guy in class, but now in the final lesson I was about to have the most humiliating public canning, and worse than all the bad guys over the last three years. Mr D. said nothing more, then walked the full length of the desk/ lab bench and put my paper to one side, right at the end. After all the rest of the marks were read out, Mr D. looked over to me and said, *"Come here"*, so I walked out in disgrace and unease.

"Are you playing a joke on me?" Mr D., asked, *"No Mr D.,"* I replied, at least as confused and bewildered as he was. In previous lessons in the weeks leading up to the test Mr D. had been covering the questions, and he reminded me how I had been getting them mostly right. He cited a question and answer on something like poles of electromagnetic force, and asked me, *"So why don't you give those answers in the test"*? Mr D.'s favourite cane was lurking in the background.

"Don't know, which ones?" I asked. *"Any of them"* said Mr D., and continued *"Ok, do the answers for me and the class now, from the top"*. My luck was in and somehow I got the first number of questions right, much to my relief. Mr D. began by writing up the answers. Next he got me to stand on a stool to write on the board, (it wasn't possible for me to reach that high even though the other boys in my class were tall enough to reach without using a lab stool). Following a few more questions that I gave the right answers for, he asked me, *"Why didn't you do the questions in the test like that, it's like you can't read, but when I ask you them you answer the questions perfectly...What's wrong with you?"*

The trial wasn't over as by now Mr D., was in despair and said, *"All your writing is getting mixed up"* and then he told me to answer the remaining questions from standing in the corner. Somehow my luck continued and I got the last dozen or so over 90% right first time, and perhaps more with some interaction. Mr D. wrote the last answers up the on the board, assisted every so often by support from the others in the class who like me were otherwise silent.

What the final question was is no longer recalled, however what is remembered is as he wrote my answer up he got a small bit of the maths wrong. Before being able to stop myself, I corrected him by saying; *"Per second, per second, Mr D.".* In that moment it looked as though a considerable caning was about to take place, but also in the same moment he realised time division had occurred twice and got my drift. *"You're right, I can't believe it!"* Mr D. said. *"There was time, and there, I missed that, yes per second per second, you're right!"* Mr D. slumped onto his lab chair and looked at me then the class in complete disbelief. *"If you can correct my maths, why can't you do that on paper in the test?"* He said baffled and exasperated. *"You've had a blank, a complete blank. You must be a dyslexic or something", "Why didn't you even get one question right?"* It was difficult to say and I had no answer. For a start what was a dyslexic anyway? There was no suggestion or reason to offer, believing I had read the questions as they were intended to be read.

Years later it transpired somewhere between 1977 and 1980 an English Teacher had once suggested I might have dyslexia at a parents evening, but nothing else followed.

Since my mother informed me of being impacted by Distaval/ *Thalidomide,* I realised she had known all along there was a link to my learning difficulties and struggles with reading and writing. Her awareness was heightened from being a highly in tune infant and junior teacher. By the time of her passing both of us knew each other was aware

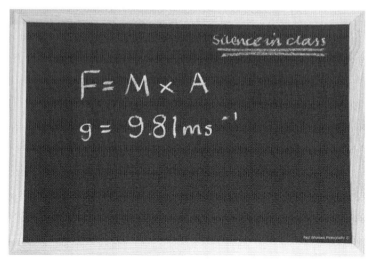

A scientific quest for understanding eventually provided some unexpected answers

Distaval/ *Thalidomide* was the cause and reason behind the myriad of my subtle learning difficulties. A situation that has plagued my life, as reading and writing underpins so much more learning potential and opens doors for further opportunities or not where limitations are encountered.

What would that be like for a mother who took the tablets in good faith? My mother's intuition had picked up on the subtle pervasive detrimental impact Distaval/ *Thalidomide* had caused in my reading and writing struggles.

The underlying issues were present from the earliest of times during my school education, and beyond. For a long time I have known not to trust my own reading or writing. The knock to personal confidence is difficult to fully explain. It somehow affects and undermines every aspect of life, and all aspirations creating self-doubt on many levels.

Out of these issues came some more twists and turns that couldn't have been imagined before becoming aware of my Distaval/*Thalidomide* exposure. However this awareness ultimately would lead to hugely more profound discoveries, revealed in greater detail in the following chapter. In my mother's very final times I sensed she knew I had already been working on ways to evidence this, and in time would highlight Dyslexia with connections to Distaval/*Thalidomide*.

Today I couldn't confirm what the correct spelling was on junior school spelling tests, but now understand very different interpretations and perspectives on years of education including Dairy or Diary?

"Tenacity: If you get up one more time than you fall,
you will make it through" [2]

Chinese Proverb

6

Mapping Connections by Connection Mapping

This chapter could have been titled, discovering the undiscoverable by applying something invisible. Following my awareness of exposure to Distaval/ *Thalidomide* I increasingly had a sense the drug was responsible for a lifelong dyslexia type condition. Early on it seemed difficult to find a link to Distaval/ *Thalidomide* exposure and my learning and brain impairments. All my research ran into dead ends, and I found little on harms to the brain resulting from *Thalidomide* dating back to the 1960's, although research 20 years later in the 1980's implicated *Thalidomide* harms extended to a range of brain impairments. Conclusions were *Thalidomide* exposure during pregnancy affected not only the morphological development of the limbs of the foetus, but in addition the functions of its central nervous system, causing hearing impairment, other cranial nerve symptoms, mental retardation and epilepsy [1].

All the same even this data looks as if as if was only based on underestimating recognised *Thalidomide* Embryopathy, and thus restricted by the constraints of the mythical limited 9 week sensitive period. Hence there wasn't much consideration of *Thalidomide* harms on the developing brain in later pregnancy, for example re; 16 weeks of foetal development. Plus pre-dating research was too general and thin on detail for relating to my situation, but valuable insights came from some of my earlier life experience. These provided transferable applications from the unexpected, and enabled substantial revelations on the issues concerned.

Refrigerator temperature monitoring might not initially appear to offer any great likelihood for revealing momentous insights into damage caused by Distaval/ *Thalidomide*, during weeks 16 to 20 of pregnancy. However such dismissal would considerably underestimate its potential. In the UK around the late 1980's early 1990s food hygiene became a significant national concern. It was famously brought to the public attention by Edwina Curry, the then Minister for Agriculture, regarding high levels of a strain of the food poisoning bacterium Salmonella in egg production [2].

Unpredicted revelations of temperature mapping

At around this time I worked in an assistant role in Environmental Health, and food hygiene. Objectives were to help introduce practical down to earth concepts promoting food safety with both businesses and the community. The process of measuring and assigning temperatures to set places is known as Temperature Monitor Mapping (TMM), and was a good way of engaging with food businesses. A warm/ 'hot' spot reduces the length of time food can be stored both in terms of safety and quality.

Latter in the mid 1990's I worked with a micro-biologist colleague on an ongoing activity concerning vacuum packed cheese. He combined simple tools of pH analysis with TMM for assessing a persistent cross contamination issue, somehow bypassing computer controlled safeguards. TMM is basic, but can offer real world practical ways of building up complex and insightful detail of otherwise invisible and unknowable situations.

As much as any physical health gains, bicycle riding is a time in the day I use for recharging my mind. The hypnotic pedalling combined with moving forward creates a relaxed mental state, allowing both free thoughts and resourceful thinking. On an otherwise indifferent ride a range of thoughts occurred to me around the concept of mapping my brain like a refrigerator; upper, middle and lower shelves etc. This would show things not visible, through things not able to be seen, by a mapping process. Simple things often turn out to be the best and most dependable, the only question was would it demonstrate eco validity, i.e. would it work in real life?

In the early 2000's I had a dyslexia assessment with the Open University. This revealed I had severe Irlen syndrome or scotopic sensitivity syndrome; something where a mass

Paul Whymark Photography ©

Mapping enables the road ahead to be predicted

of abstract characters close together swim, pulse and jump around due to the hemmed in proximity to each other. On learning this I understood the numerous reading charts I kept being tested on at school and hospital visits had been producing false negatives. This is because the single letters are spaced wide apart and do not get jumbled up with other letters close by, and therefore were not testing my ability to actually read in real text. Yet my teachers and doctors at the hospital in childhood would have been completely unaware of this.

For the first 30 years of my life I had assumed this happened to everybody, and that it was just that I was not as good at dealing with it compared to everyone else. Ironic but Irlen syndrome was identified in California in the 1970's and 1980s during the same time frame I was struggling at school [3]. Colour overlays or tinted lenses are used to counter or at least partly counter the swimming effect, and different colours work for different people. These allow better contrast and reduce glare. The best colour tint for me is a light orange colour much like the hue of the Oakley sunglasses orange lenses I had been using for some years to improve all-purpose vision. There was no doubt my eye function in general is ok, but clearly something is occurring in my brain to thwart sequencing of abstract characters in close proximity.

The process of a dual or two stage brain mapping is in essence is very simple. Like TMM it starts by mapping a single dimension. In my case a particular deficit onto the relevant brain function area. This is then mapped onto a secondary dimension, i.e. mapping the relevant brain area(s) to foetal brain development in the relevant time window; i.e. in my case weeks 16 to 20.

A notable part of the brain used to focus on fine detail/ abstracts, and differentiation of letters, numbers and symbols is right at the back of the optical lobe, at the back of the brain. Located under the optical extrusion on the skull bone, it is sometimes referred to as the visual reading area or primary visual cortex and its surrounding association area [4, p386-p390]. Association areas in the brain, communicate both with a primary area and other motor cortex areas, and assist in analysing and recognising sensory inputs, hence the significance to the primary visual area [4, p386-p390]. Damage to these areas can mean more subtle impairments, as the main functional area may still operate to an extent, but not to the level of complete functioning. It could be other areas of the brain are forced into a frenzy of over compensating, and this too may exacerbate the situation.

Secondary mapping considered whether the optical

lobe develops in weeks 16 to 20 of human gestation? This area of the brain does develop in this time frame and to a considerable extent [5, p24-p25] [6, p54-59] [7, p54-66]. No surprises the occipital lobe plays a real part in visual deciphering of letters and numbers. In general it is the case the brains gyrus (outer areas) undergo significant development during this same time window, and include areas that enable language and higher functioning [4, p386-p390] [5, 24-p25] [6, p54-59] [7, p54-66]. There is a network of brain functions in a number of areas that interacts as a system to facilitate language in all its forms by utilizing phonological coding. This is sometimes referred to the phonological loop, and helps with learning and language acquisition by utilizing working memory while information is being processed. It draws on and involves long-term Memory. Pioneering work by Alan Baddeley for Cambridge University found the phonological loop plays a valuable role in language acquisition [8] [9, p156-p160]. The phonological loop is a key component of working memory enabling speech based information to be held and sub vocalisation processes [9, p534]. Thus as the function underpins language to some extent, then it too becomes impaired and hence hinders further new language acquisition.

At 16 weeks the brain's central fissure has not formed and the cerebral hemispheres are smooth. It is significant the temporal and frontal cortex general mass has also not yet fully developed [10, p267]. Specific areas including Wernickers region are contained within these not yet fully formed areas that are still otherwise trying to develop at weeks 16 to 20. The dramatic development in foetal brain gestation during this time frame is graphically photographed in Marjorie England's text books; A colour Atlas of Life Before Birth Normal Foetal Development

(1983) [6, p54-p65]; plus, Life before Birth Second Ed (1996) [7, p54-p66]; plus, A colour Atlas of the Brain and Spinal Cord [5, p22-p25].

It is a bit like building a computer network and leaving out some key components. The computer parts may still work in some respects, but it will never be able to functional as well as it would have if all the components been put together as intended.

Dr. Parkins, an Educational Psychologist undertook my first dyslexia assessment in 1996, in a time before I was aware of Distaval/ *Thalidomide* exposure in me had occurred. He described my situation as follows; *"You (Paul) have a good 'computer', it's just your 'scanner' and your 'printer' are not working that well...so you will have to take more time for everything you do".* He was right, and I have to accept things take me longer. For reading and writing this is about 4 to 5 times longer when I am fresh and not tired. Nonetheless knowing this stops me from giving up, as if I work at it harder and longer, then eventually things come together. The dyslexia assessment Dr. Parkins conducted was comprehensive and identified specific elements of my cognitive impairments. Conclusions were that I have considerable deficits in aspects of language recognition, and comprehension construction when reading and writing; plus an even greater deficit when compared to my verbal lexical ability.

It did not occur to me until well into the 2000's the information in this 1996 diagnostic dyslexia report could be mapped on to brain areas. However on discovering Irlen syndrome mapped onto parts of the brain specific to visual word reading, I realised all relevant areas could also be mapped onto development of the foetal brain during weeks 16 to 20 [5, p24-p25] [6, p54-p59] [7, p54-p66]. At this point I

Walls built on foundations of sand will in the end fracture and give way

understood universally mapping brain functions onto foetal development would show all the areas of my cognitive deficits; and it does in relation to all my deficits, but only in these areas, not any others. By now real and significant fault lines in the wall of *Thalidomide* misinformation were beginning to open up.

Brain mapping was previously considered by Paul Broca (1824 to 1880), who made a notable discovery of particular relevance. In 1861 he undertook an autopsy on a man who suffered a stroke causing the man to lose the ability to speak. An autopsy of the man revealed stroke damage in a specific area of his brain. Broca identified this was the reason for speech impairment. Damage caused by the stroke was on the left hand side in the cerebral cortex, around where the left temporal and left frontal lobe meet and became known as Broca's Area [11, p9] [12, p48, p51, p54-p55].

Contemporary research reveals speech and language functions points to greater dispersion within the brain than a single point. However all accounts include the significance of Broca's area for language and reading. My dyslexia assessment had shown very significant written and reading language impairments specific to dysfunction in the Broca's area, including internal sub vocalisation for reading. No surprise the optical lobe like the Broca's area of the brain significantly develops in weeks 16 to 20 of gestation. Foetal brain development in this period applies for cerebral Hemispheres involved in speech and language in general; plus the frontal lobe areas responsible for short-term and working memory. Both of these functions are essential for language, yet in me are very low compared to the average.

An area of the brain called Wernickers Area develops too during this same time frame. On a further dyslexia assessment, the assessor observed I had the tendency for *"word/ number sequences salad"*. This means writing/ reading where lots of things get chopped up and put down in some erratic order and sometimes repeatedly whilst omitting other words. He advised this was typical of a Wernickers dysfunction. Yet no matter how careful, I am not able to prevent such sequencing irregularities as they happen without me realising. This is to the point of being unaware of it even when reading back material some time later. The assessor informed me he saw this sort of presentation in alcoholics or people born to mothers who drank heavily. My mother was exceedingly tea total, and my drinking has always been very modest, especially by society's average levels.

The Wernickers area of the brain has been assigned a number of functions over the years and different research indicates slightly different things [12, p48] [4, p386-p390] however it is increasingly seen as enhancing other functions. Themes in general point to this part of the brain being highly

significant in assisting new learning, and or specifics in
language. In laypersons terms I see the Wernickers area as
a turbo boost to assisting language and new learning. No
surprises then the Wernickers area development occurs in
weeks 16 to 20 of foetal development; only clearly in me it
did not, like all the other areas of my brain that also show
dysfunction or reduced ability [4, p386-p390] [5, p24-p25] [6, p54-p59] [7, p54-p66].

"The Humane Foetus tho no bigger than a Green Pea, yet is finifhed with all its parts" [7, inside 1st page]

[Antonj van Leeuwenhoek, 1683].

Towards the end of my schooling I recall a teacher who
had been teaching for years saying, *"It's like they have
put something in the water, but haven't told anyone"*. Her
incidental comments concerned what would today be
referred to as dyslexia, but back then had started to be
aired and was referred to and termed as word blindness.
Looking back it did appear as if a wave of children born
in the 1960's had an increased range of reading issues,
although nothing specifically was said or done for me.

Years later my teachers seemingly irrelevant throw
away line of; *"putting something in the water"*, has a
much darker more sinister possibility when considering
Thalidomide. The 1960's drug companies were in complete
denial about any safety risks from physical harms resulting
from *Thalidomide*, let alone concerning its potential to
impair language development. Even the most questioning
medical perspectives still assumed safety during later

pregnancy. Add to the mix an inadequate recall that left many tablets on pharmacy shelves and in people's homes, with a backdrop of years of advertising the drug as "completely safe" and "atoxic" [13, 14, 15, 16]. It would not be unreasonable to wonder if *Thalidomide* was at least part of the reason behind a notable increase in dyslexia during my schooling era. In addition who knows what long term genetic variance it may have caused? In the 1960's women not uncommonly took a calming or hypnotic tablet of which there were various for wide ranging reasons. How many mothers took even only one *Thalidomide* tablet for a headache or insomnia later in pregnancy that resulted in their baby being given a life time of sub clinical dyslexic brain impairment?

Another interesting insight concerns how on being born I was unable to feed and began to starve, although as luck had it somehow after about two weeks I managed to learn. All the same at the time my mother was understandably distressed as I had lost a considerable proportion of my body weight, and there wasn't been a lot of me to start with. A baby's ability to feed is innate, but this suggests only so long as the brain's hardware has fully formed. Areas of the brain that play a major role in the suckling action of a baby are areas controlling the lips tongue and mouth movements, including swallowing. No great surprise to discover these are controlled by brain areas on the motor and sensory cortex related and involved in language and speech, clearly as all are related to coordinated mouth and tongue motor movements. These regions in the brain are located both right and especially on the left hand side near to the Broca's area involved in facilitating language [4, p386-p390].

Development in these areas occurs in weeks 16-20 of foetal brain development. It is important to appreciate the size and scale of foetal brain formation during this time. At 16 weeks the foetus is still very small indeed. From the top of the head to end of spine is approximately 12.5cm. The head proportion of the foetus is only about 1/3rd of its total length and therefore, c. 3.8cm. Hence the internal skull cavity where the brain resides is yet even smaller still. At 16 weeks the entire total foetal brain size would be c.1.5cm x c1.5cm x c.3.0cm = c.6.75 cm^3 [7, p62], and the area's affected in me would at the time probably have been c.10% of that, i.e. 0.675cm^3 (6.75 mm^3). The most minuet intricate blood vessels and circulatory network supply these extraordinarily delicate areas of brain tissues, and consequently are very susceptible to damage from the harsh destructive action of Distaval/*Thalidomide*; as is explained in greater detail in later chapters of this book.

Tests in rats in the 1960's by MacKenzie and McGrath, found *Thalidomide* absorption was very rapidly transferred to the brain, within about 15 minutes and peak concentrations within half an hour [17]. In addition note absorption/ sedative effects of *Thalidomide* in humans have been deemed as significantly greater, i.e. 50 to 60 times more than in rodents [18, p189-p191]. Hence observing an arteriogram of blood supply in the foetus reveals how *Thalidomide* would be instantly taken by the blood stream into the developing foetuses brain [7, p112].

To what extent and percentage left and right brain differentiation of functions are complete, or not, in foetal brain development at weeks 16 is not something I have been able to entirely discover. Yet with my preference for left foot for football and left hand for a computer mouse, but opposite for writing, plus other right and left right contradictions raises questions; perhaps an opportunity for post graduate study?

Paul Broca and others since ancient times have also worked on brain mapping, and there are no claims to be able to hold a candle to the above mentioned towering intellects. All the same a stumbled on *'Paulo-Dual Mapping Process'* opens up possibilities of considering implications back to foetal brain development through connection mapping by mapping connections.

'If you would understand anything, Observe its beginning and also its development' [19]

Aristotle

7

Chasing Dragonflies and a Trip
Back to 1968/ 69

Dragonflies represent a heritage of ancient life forms, although they have morphed and evolved somewhat over the millennia. Perhaps dragonflies do not represent an obvious starting point for discovering profound untold accounts of *Thalidomide* harms and damage, but as things worked out they offered a great deal more than might be expected.

Earliest forms of dragonfly species were Protodonatan with huge wingspans of up to c. 70cm [1]. They date back to Carboniferous times somewhere between 300

Dragonflies and Thalidomide secrets

million and 70 million years ago. Some of these evolved into Meganisoptera [2, p17] the now extinct order of giant insects. Out of this group came the species seen today. They originated from early forms of damselflies, Zygoptera taken from the Greek, meaning *similar wings* and Anisozygoptera appeared in the Permian Era. Dragonflies are classified as Anisoptera from Greek, meaning *'dissimilar wings'* [3, p1-p2].

During early 2008 dragonflies and natural history were not remotely in my thinking, but instead how I was going to get by with the increasingly foreboding economic downturn. It had made life highly challenging, and with no other support it halted my self-build aspirations. Alternative education options at the time appeared to be the most sensible and wise, but in hindsight continuing with the self build plans would have been a much better way forward. However at the time it left over half a year to get by and therefore I sought ways to use the time constructively and if at all possible not to slide any further.

Life's up's and down's are unpredictable, and looking back the summers of 2008 and 2009 working and volunteering at a Field Studies Council education centre, were the best of times for more than a decade. There was an energy hard to describe or put my finger on, but felt continually present. Driving to interview along a country road I checked the map, but it didn't have enough detail to specify the location. Ahead was a bridge carrying the main 'A' road overhead. Next I caught sight of a round stone ball on top of a square stone pillar. Even though I didn't know this was the centre or could even see it might be I instantly knew it would be. The reason for being so certain was uncanny. About 40 years earlier aged only two or maybe three years old, I had been driven along the same road in my grandfathers Morris Minor 1.0 L around 1968, or perhaps 1969.

Yet intriguingly my memory was from travelling in the opposite direction, looking out the front then the side, and then the back window of his Morris Minor 1.0 L. In that moment of 2008 instantly I knew an old tree would appear, then just after, down a long driveway would be an old white house.

Exactly as I recalled the above played out. Could that 1968/ '69 moment subconsciously have been etched deep into my mind through the car radio with Jim Morrison and the Doors at their zenith? On reflection my grandfather probably didn't listen that much to the Doors; and also as at the time I was only two or perhaps nearly three years old, it probably had nothing to do with the late 1960's music and counter culture scene.

The main work of the Field Studies Council (F.S.C.) is

Memories of Paul's Grandfathers Morris Minor
(Photography support: Charles Ware Morris Minor Centre Ltd., Bristol)

engaging people in education about the natural world. Consequently my work involved ongoing preparation tasks for field study activities; cleaning and tidying field test tubes, hand lenses, sweep nets, clip boards, buckets, wellington boots etc. Copious records of species counts were also thoughtfully kept, along with weather and temperature recordings, then forwarded to national and wider monitoring. Energy and water usage data was collected for valuable conservation work, such as environmental impact assessments. All the jobs were enjoyed as the actives were worthwhile and shared with good company.

F.S.C. information guides and educational materials are first class, colourful and stimulate informed thinking, see F.S.C. publications [4]. Their range of UK identification guides opens up a whole new world of reptiles, mammals, birds, fish, plants, fungi, lichens, and the same for insects and other invertebrates. F.S.C. guides often explore the identification of different species at various stages of their life cycle.

Around 2008 I came across a set of fascinating identification fact sheets as a pilot for a national programme of public involvement. One such area of ecological exploration, concerned lichen growth for assessing air quality. Easy-to-understand scientific information about air quality can be interpreted by simply looking at lichen growth forms and comparing them to a chart showing each one's pollution tolerance. Monitoring involves assessing the types and propensity of lichens, their colour and quality. Lichens are categorized as bioindicators. It was not a term I had previously been aware of, even though I appreciated some of the underlying concepts. Change to eco-systems over time can produce bioindicators

Paul Whymark Photography ©

Ultimately biomarker evidence can't be denied

such as lichens that can exhibit consequences e.g. presentations of reduced or expanded growth, or a change in species assemblage. Lichen can indicate metal pollution, lead for example [5, p377-p419].

Many species can be regarded as bioindicators because their presence or absence often reflects qualities or harmful impacts on or within the environment. Pollution can produce many different affects and consequences of bioindication in an organism, including reduction in size.

Life in all its forms adapts and is affected by its environment as in the case of the white and black Pepper Moths in northern England. The ratio between the two varieties changed due to a reduction of soot/ coal smog in the atmosphere. Numbers of the black mutation of this moth decreased as cleaner air levels reduced darker deposits on habitat like tree bark, leaving the white version better camouflaged, which therefore increased in population. Disguise is the main way the moths avoid being predated, thus why lighter moth numbers expanded as the darker moth numbers became predicated. This scenario illustrates how by paying attention and considering feedback, we can monitor an absence of something as a bioindicator to detect environmental change [6].

The Lime Hark-moth is another wonder of nature with its amazing camouflage. It provides a noteworthy reminder that when an environment gets damaged, a wider ecosystem is also harmed or lost. Hence if lime trees disappear then obviously so too Lime Hawk-moths, along with other integrated biodiversity. As humanity and food provision is ultimately tied into ecology, preservation of bio-diversity is a no brainer.

"Ecology? Look it up! You're involved" [7]

Green Peace, 1969

Nature is beautiful and we are also part of it
(Photography: Lime hawk moth on a lime tree)

Dragonflies (Anisoptera) are less of favoured bioindicator species but do have thresholds of tolerance to pollution, revealed by lack of development and growth. The typical time dragonflies take to develop underwater is nine months to two years, and some sub species can stay under water for up to five years [3, p1-p2]. A specialist in dragonfly monitoring advised, where the environment was less conducive it may result in extended developmental timescales. One effect in the environment often causes secondary indirect consequences elsewhere.

Dragonflies usually are not a particular designated bioindicator species, but they illustrate how being submerged in an environment for a prolonged period, means bioindicator effects reveal more than hi-tech gadgets may offer from only small snapshots of time. In practice nature's feedback is a real time recorder, and discloses more subtle detail about response levels, as well as what is being responded to in the environment. Ponds at F.S.C. Preston Montford showed various species were to be at different stages of their life cycle through the seasons. Pond dipping studies together with field guide charts are great ways to introduce the concept of biomarkers and bioindicators, and what they can reveal.

From these activities I realised the more complex organisms and species, so the risk of harm increases, because more complexity is involved in the developmental stages. It provided very real lateral insight into appreciating the full potential harms of Distaval/ *Thalidomide*, during all stages of human embryonic and foetal development, with endless complex stages to go through.

Exposure on an unborn baby from Distaval/ *Thalidomide* at weeks 16 of pregnancy produces a quite different set of bio-impacts compared to impacts during weeks 5, 8, 12, or 14, for example. Exposure to a toxin or teratogen may result in quite different consequential presentations across different developmental stage time lines. In the case of *Thalidomide* inadequate and the wrong conclusions were made because the right questions were not satisfactorily defined, let alone adequately answered. This left the mythical limits of only an eccentric mix of specific days within the first so called "9 week sensitive period", to go unchallenged for the last five decades.

Insights into biomarkers and nature's bioindicators revealed how empowering questions could be asked, by using only a little lateral thinking. Questions raised provided even more profound answers. During this time I came to realise the much deeper and more significant concept, and I moved from thinking Distaval/ *Thalidomide* had produced only specific impacts to realising it had impacted on every single developing cell while at the stage of being a 16 week foetus. Thus Distaval/*Thalidomide* exposure had left my total being as a biomarker/bioindicator, freeze framed in a moment of time from March 1966 for all of my life thereafter.

As for freeze framing photographs of dragonflies in my spare time during the summers of 2008 and 2009, it took patience and provided frustration in equal measure, but gained some enjoyable shots and good memories.

With broadened conceptual horizons and new levels of constructive free thinking it showed when humans ask the right questions in the right ways, and are prepared to listen, then nature always provides the right answers. Unlike corporations, governments and individuals with conflicts of vested interest, nature never hides or miss represents anything; but instead reveals the full picture and insight through biomarkers and bioindication.

Paul Whymark Photography ©

Enchanting dragonfly revelations

Childhood rides 40 years earlier in my grandfathers Morris Minor 1.0 L, provided a dependably good premonition for the summer's opportunities of chasing dragonflies and a trip back to 1968/ 69.

"It is horrifying that we have to fight Our own government to save the environment" [8]

Ansel Adams, Photographer

8

Unanswered Questions in Australia

Following my mother's disclosure of Distaval/ *Thalidomide* at weeks 16 to 20 of her pregnancy with me, I gradually began making initial enquires and personal research into the drug and its history. Around the early 2000's like many people I had no internet access, although like increasing numbers of people I attended introductory IT training at a local college.

It was here I first got to use a now very well known ubiquitous search engine, to seek information on

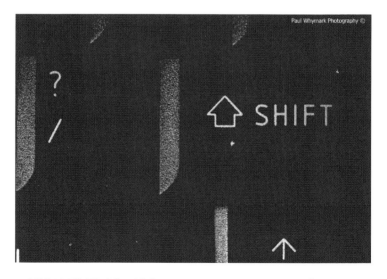

Mid 1960's *Thalidomide* later pregancy use promotions have now disappeared

Thalidomide history and the consequences of exposure.
It didn't take long to realise something or things were
clearly amiss with information available. There were similar
general themes implying the drug was stopped around
1962, although some countries had later dates of around
1965, Ireland and Italy for example. There was some
information about a "withdrawal" from the wholesale
market but little else to suggest a satisfactory recall or
complete ban.

Yet it was always clear to me my mother would never
have taken the drug, unless it was available and given
to her advised as a safe drug. On occasions when she
talked to me about the subject I would ask when Distaval/
Thalidomide stopped being given out. Her response on
timelines was always a bit vague, but advised of not
taking it during her pregnancy with my sister, suggesting
somewhere between 1966 and 1969. In addition my
mother informed the Distaval tablets she had taken were...
"Yellow...gold or golden coloured", along with another
seemingly incidental piece of information; *"It* (Distaval/
*Thalidomide) was given out for use later on in pregnancy,
by then (early 1966)".*

Specific searches for notices and articles
communicating bans or recalls were sought, but they
were strangely none existent. In addition I could not
find anything to counter or warn of risks for use in later
pregnancy either, despite repeated searching. In later times
my enquiry extended to various libraries and document
archives of old newspapers, journals and materials from
back in the 1960s. These too were equally scant on
warnings or safety information to the public. Although one
article I saw from the early 1960's had reports of Distaval/
Thalidomide being given out on trains as sedatives, but

here too without any hint of warnings or advice on safety for women who were, or could be pregnant.

My mother informed me the tablets were a yellow, golden colour and so I searched for this with mixed results. Nothing of note came up for 1966, and so I decided to try 1965. After all it was only 9 weeks after the end of 1965 when they were given to her. Typing key words like: Yellow + Gold/ Golden + 1965 brought up a handful of web pages. Some of these showed advertisements or sort of promotion articles written about Distaval/ *Thalidomide*, not for the UK, but for Australia and linked to Distillers Company Bio–chemicals (Australia) Ltd.

The feel conveyed *Thalidomide* had not been proven to be unsafe, yet Distillers Company Bio-chemicals Ltd claimed to be such good guys, they now offered a new ridiculous level of over cautious guideline for safe use after weeks 12/ 13 in pregnancy. The overriding impression I received from these advertisements/ articles around 1964 and 1965 was of a new adapted market focus, promoting Distaval/*Thalidomide* for later use in pregnancy; because they claimed it, *"continued to be one of the safest drugs ever".*

A further search for links to Australia typing in use in later pregnancy brought some articles up, and some may have been the same as above. Instantly I was struck by specific recommendation for use later in pregnancy after weeks 12 or 13, to *"reduce the extreme stress a woman is placed under during pregnancy".* The articles or advertisements by Distillers Company Bio-Chemicals Ltd Australia were clearly a contradiction to total ban in 1962, and one I saw would have been around as late as 1967 or 1968. Out of these searches made over several months I occasionally discovered further web pages referring

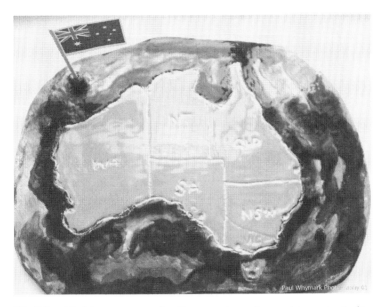

Thalidomide history can easily disappear in a place as big as Australia
(Photography support: Vanessa Clark helped in producing ceramic
map tile)

to Distaval/ *Thalidomide* for 1964 for Ireland, Australia,
Rhodesia (now Zimbabwe) and South Africa.

When I was about 14 years old a seemingly insignificant
situation occurred, when some of my mother's friends
visited. They hadn't seen each other for a while, and
immediately got deep into conversation. As I entered the
kitchen my mother came in from another door, and was
still talking with her friends. Her comments back to the
women in the other room conveyed how she had taken it
during her pregnancy with me, and that it was still being
used in Australia at the time. I looked at her a bit startled
and asked what *"it"* was? My mother said nothing as such
but filled a kettle with water and put it on, then she came
over to me rubbed my face gave me a big hug, and went

back into the room with her friends shutting the door behind her. This was somewhat unfathomable but I gave no real further thought to this seemingly irrelevant incident. Until that is about 20 years later when I unearthed web pages promoting Distaval/ *Thalidomide* use in Australia during the mid 1960's, for use in later pregnancy beyond 12 to 13 weeks, referencing gold/ yellow tablets.

Today these web pages have completely vanished without a trace, and I don't know if they are still out there, or whether they have been entirely removed? However they were around for some time after I stopped attending the Wye Room IT classes in the autumn of 2002, most likely until around 2006 to 2008, perhaps even later? It was probably around 2010/ 2011 when I again more actively sought to find them, by repeated use of different search engines including Australian ones, but all to no avail.

An archive correspondence on health.wa.gov.au revealed some both telling and disturbing aspects on the dubious conduct of Distillers Company Bio-chemicals Ltd UK. Circular N. 21 (8th December 1961) with an accompanying letter dated 29th November 1961, sent out by Distillers Company Bio Chemicals (Australia PTY) Limited, Campbell Street, Artamon, NSW, Australia [1]. The correspondence related to Australia and New Zealand, with the former supplying the latter, it made no admissions or acknowledgments there was any underling problems or safety issues concerning Distaval/ *Thalidomide*.

Instead its feel and spin is of the exact opposite, claiming; 1. Evidence was only, *"circumstantial"* and 2. *"(There have been no reports arising in Great Britain (UK), either chemically or pharmacologically)"*[1]. [Both of these claims, 1 and 2 were and are very misleading, yet Distillers Company Bio-chemicals Ltd (Australia and UK) continued to communicate these sentiments for years after; and for certain had done nothing to revoke or counter this position before my mother consumed Distaval/ *Thalidomide* in early 1966 four years later.]

Sinisterly the word; *"quote"* was hand written left of the typed heading, *"WITHDRAWAL OF DISTAVAL"* [1]. In many ways this single handwritten added word, *"quote"*, gives away the more disconcerting insight into the real aim of the communication; i.e. an arm twisting protocol for all involved to be on message. At the time it enabled *Thalidomide* drug companies to initiate their spun propaganda script. By using the term "withdrawal", it allowed *Thalidomide* to be kept in the wings ready to go back on to the market for something in the future. "Withdrawal" did not communicate the more significant semantics of unsafe or levels of risk of harm, for adults or developing babies. This was the preliminary ground work to facilitate a seamless return to the market for other uses in the future, thus avoiding scrutiny and without too many questions being asked.

The carefully alternative worded Australian communications very much concurred with what my mother had advised me in her final times. This was how Distaval/*Thalidomide* was recommended for use after weeks 12 or 13 during later pregnancy, to counter the, *"stress and anxiety caused by pregnancy"*. Morning sickness as my mother put it had been, *"going on forever by 16 weeks"*. It's understandable this alone would have caused extra stress and anxiety, if not even some mild depression; – something else Distaval/ *Thalidomide* was simultaneously used for. As a dedicated infant school teacher this no doubt provided enough stress for her, without additional ongoing morning sickness.

In the prior mentioned Australian communication

by Distillers Company Bio-chemicals Australia Ltd., "withdrawal" of their *Thalidomide* products they produced and distributed included; Valgia, Tensival and Valgraine. The latter, Valgraine, was also sold in the UK, and was a yellow/ golden type colour (perhaps appearing as a bit sunny orange in advertisements), and in particular targeted the migraine market; *"The powerful new partnership against migraine", and "each tablet contains: Thalidomide ('Distaval'), 12.5mg, Ergotamine Tartrate B.P. 1.0mg"* [2].

It is not difficult to appreciate how Valgraine/ *Thalidomide* with this feel would most likely quietly sit on many pharmacy shelves for years to come. Another additional menacing factor was the drugs alter ego, alias, and dual/ multi persona of being only a harmless headache tablet marketed as Valgraine for migraines; but in addition could at the same time be seen as the widely claimed "atoxic" and "completely safe" Distaval/ *Thalidomide*.

Advertising for Distaval/*Thalidomide* had for years declared universal safety, with an implied high level of safety for all vulnerable groups, including for use on the elderly and infirm, plus pregnant women. One advertisement tells the narrative of an elderly man, who somehow took a huge over dose without any harmful effects, (or so it was claimed?) [3]. A double page spread in the BMJ on 23rd January 1960, had wild 'indisputable' accolades, accredited under the banner "DISTAVAL IS SAFE" [4]. These were wrong in the extreme.

Although few advertisements in history have ever been more manipulative, despicable and untrustworthy than the one claiming; *'this child's life may depend on the safety of Distaval'"*, picturing a toddler exploring a medicine cabinet holding a bottle of Distaval/*Thalidomide* [5]. An advertisement used at various times, including in the BMJ on 24th June 1961. It and other advertisements implanted subliminal universal safety of *Thalidomide* in peoples' minds. It ensured unconscious semantics of total safety from young to old were well established by the time when *Thalidomide* "withdrawal" from the wholesale market slowly and begrudgingly began, right at the end of 1961 into 1962.

The advertisement for Distaval Forte a *Thalidomide* increased dose, quoted *"...the safe day time sedative which is equally safe in hypnotic doses by night, 'Distaval' is especially suitable for infants, the aged and patients under severe emotional stress."* [6]; the phrase, *"under severe emotional stress"* was the same as I had seen relating to recommended use during later pregnancy for use after weeks 12/13, in Australia in the mid 1960's.

"Advertising is the rattling of a stick inside a swill bucket" [7]

George Orwell

Doctors in the UK and probably in Australia were far less inhibited or restrained in what they prescribed, before The Medicines Act of 1968 [8]. Even post 1968 some aspects of the Act may not have been fully implemented until around 1971. Prior to the Act record keeping was not required, especially in the case of *Thalidomide* because it was seen as safer than aspirin. It should come as no surprise therefore even five to six years post "withdrawal" from the wholesaler Distaval/ *Thalidomide* was still being used by a well meaning but an inadequately advised medical profession.

The official Irish *Thalidomide* website formerly

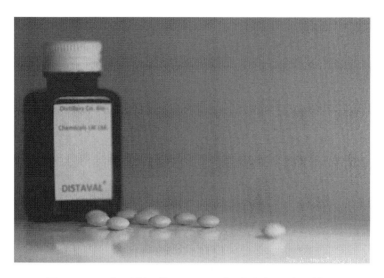

Unaccounted gold/ yellow **Distaval**/ Thalidomide tablets

presented a time line date up to 1965, but around 2011 to 2012, this 1965 date was removed as silently as a falling snowflake. Hence the impression it left was no *Thalidomide* harms occurred in Ireland after around 1962. However not all 1965 references to *Thalidomide* cases in Ireland, were totally sanitized or airbrushed out. One reference is contained in Compensation for *Thalidomide* Survivors April 2010 Report, Prepared for the Minister for Health and Children, by the State Claims Agency page 4, 13 [9].

At some point I found a PDF [10]; with a link to Australia and yellow/ gold tablets. Quoting; *FJM LECTURE 1958, of "distaval forte" each contain 100 mg. thalidomide. The dose for hypnosis is one tablet at night. ... "in South Australia, making 36 regional faculties in all, 25 ... made in white and yellow gold by Messrs. Garrard and Co. Ltd., ...".* This did not relate to 1965 or for use in later pregnancy, and offered no other relevant information to my quest, but nonetheless confirmed existence of yellow/ gold coloured Distaval/*Thalidomide* tablets in Australia. What role Messrs. Garrard and Co. Ltd played in the 1960's with Distillers Company Bio-chemicals Ltd (Australia Pty/ UK), I have not been able to discover.

In the early 1960's Australian women had been treated like guinea pigs and given *Thalidomide* before tests on animals [11]. Like in the UK, Australia too had an inadequate recall and lack of effective public safety warnings. Mrs Tapua in Australia during 1974 visited a private doctor, and was given a prescription for morning sickness, a product produced by Distillers Company Bio-Chemicals Ltd, but didn't realise the brand contained *Thalidomide* [12], and gave birth to a baby harmed by the drug.

During October 1973 in Worcestershire, UK, two hundred *Thalidomide* tablets turned up during a campaign to uncover outdated medicines [13]. While in Sussex, UK, in 1976 further *Thalidomide* tablets turned up in a local campaign to hand in unused medicines [14]. It was commented that journalists were playing a more important role in saving children from *Thalidomide* than the health regulatory authorities in many parts of the world, and the UK was no exception.

During the early 2000's I stumbled on anecdotal accounts of some unexpected Distaval/ *Thalidomide* use. The first was for some recreational exploit as a calming agent, by early hippies at '*Happenings*' at scenes in London like where Pink Floyd played in December 1966, and similarly in California during this time. The other reports suggested Distaval/*Thalidomide* returned to Psychiatric Medicine after 1962, and included use as a sedative pre/ post electric shock therapy (E.S.T.). The psychiatric uses were somewhere around 1968 to 1971, but here too I have been unable to find these web pages in more recent times, despite repeated searching.

At Powick Psychiatric Hospital in Worcestershire between 1964 and 1972 LSD was administered for clinical procedures to 680 patients [15], using protocol established by Dr Ronald Sandison; the subject of a World in Action TV programme in 1968 [15]. It is probable others hospitals were using LSD and possibly *Thalidomide*. I sought Freedom of Information (F.O.I.) requests from a couple of Psychiatric hospitals compliance teams for research for this chapter. Unable to talk with a human being I repeatedly left my details on answer phones, but none of my calls were ever returned.

Nonetheless the drug companies had significant residual stocks of *Thalidomide* post "withdrawal" from the wholesaler, and consequently serious money tied up in these stocks. A year after the UK "withdrawal" in early 1963 a US professional psychiatry Journal [16] continued to offer positive assessments on *Thalidomide*, but without any great warnings, as if there were no health risks at all. In this context if Distaval/ Thalidomide had one way or another found its way back to psychiatric medicine either in the UK, Australia or elsewhere it would not be a surprise.

In the UK and in Australia Distaval/ *Thalidomide* originally started to be used in psychiatric medicine [11] [17]. Whether it returned in some way to psychiatric medicine in Australia post "withdrawal" from the wholesale market in 1962, I have not yet been able to substantiate.

If anybody has any information on use in later pregnancy or insight into yellow/ gold/ golden Distaval/ *Thalidomide* tablets or the role Messrs. Garrard and Co. Ltd please share such information; as Distaval connections between the UK and Australia continues to be of interest to me. From the early 2000's onwards I have had the sense there was more than official accounts divulged thus far, in a number of respects. This includes experience or awareness from back in the day, or shared accounts from those no longer with us. Likewise if you are savvy with how things work in Australia then please seek out old journals and production leads from around the mid to late 1960's, and contact former employees, medics and people from that era. Despite being 50 years on it may still be possible to shine some more daylight on failings in the UK and unanswered questions in Australia.

"An original idea; That can't be too hard The library must be full of them" [18]

Steven Fry

PART III

A Greater and Wider Awareness

9

Joining up Unseen Dots...

It could have been as early as 2006, although it may have been a bit later, perhaps around 2007 when I first contacted The *Thalidomide* Trust UK (TTUK). This was undertaken in the spirit of mutual consideration and reciprocation in an open way to share information of my situation. However it was strange because TTUK came across to me as having a very unhelpful uptight attitude of can't do won't do that felt obstinate, and caught me off guard.

At the time everything seemed to have go through the then Director of the *Thalidomide* Trust UK. It felt like a limiting gateway, a road block and unavoidable filter. My small request was for some back up, to try and help find out more about Distaval/*Thalidomide* in Australia c.1964, 1965, 1967; promoted for use later in pregnancy from weeks 12/13. It surprised me but all my encounters with TTUK felt patronising, hostile and dismissive. To try and encourage TTUK I explained how to use a well known search engine, to find the relevant web pages using terms of yellow/ gold/ golden tablets, 1964/ 1965 Australia, 12/ 13 weeks etc. At that point in time these pages and the information were still present on the internet.

Looking back now it is difficult to recall how many times and the exact dates when I contacted the TTUK, as their responses were so negative and off putting it discouraged seeking further contact or to try to work with them. Could it have been a strategy? They seemed to have their own agenda, and strangely not for the good concerning wider unaddressed *Thalidomide* issues, and as such I began referring to them as the myopic *"Thalidomide* establishment".

The negative style of engagement resulted in notable time gaps between each encounter. All of my shared communications were met with the same indifference, along with something in addition that felt distinctly more contemptuous. For example the not infrequent use of patronizing phrases, such as and furthermore, as if somehow to signify there was irrelevance twice over in the valid points I was raising. In addition there were some other curious aspects I encountered with *Thalidomide* Trust UK were difficult to fully quantify, but left me feeling decidedly queasy. For example the carefully spun stock phrases of slippery political management speak like; *Thalidomide* was *"only marketed"* in the UK between April 1959 and December 1961. Along with other management spin incorporating words like *"discontinued"*. Plus expressions like; the critical gestational period for causing *"recognised abnormality"* is between 34 to 50 days after LMP (4 weeks 6 days to 7 weeks 1 day).

All of this only side stepped the real issues. Such assertions are wildly inaccurate, but propped up a lot of other misleading claims, including 16 weeks was a time too late for *Thalidomide* to have caused adverse effects. All the above is either grossly misleading or intrinsically false, yet disappointingly has been circumvented by TTUK and other settlement entities in unison by then for over 40, and now for over 50 years.

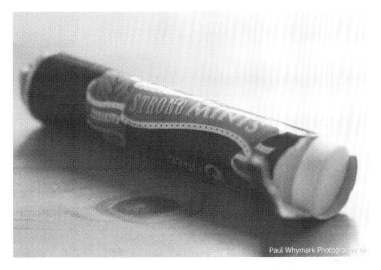

Freeing the airways can help assist clear thinking

"Life is infinitely stranger than anything of which the mind of man can invent" [1]

Sherlock Holmes

To facilitate some fresh thinking, it was time to take a deep breath. Who does the recognising, based on what methodologies, and on what assumptions?

The lack of appreciation of some fairly elementary anatomy and physiology, during embryological and foetal development unsettled me. This was to the point I began to doubt the then TTUK Director, Dr Martin Johnson, was even a medical doctor? Concerns were heightened further when I was unable to discover what medical qualifications he had or where he had trained. It raised some serious red flags, not only about the Director, but more widely concerning the entire outfit of the *Thalidomide* Trust UK. What was their real remit? What was their real purpose? What was their real brief? How had it been assigned? And by whom? Plus who or what oversees the TTUK or other settlement bodies/ organisations?

I could find no answers and it appears nobody, thus it was time to undertake some closer scrutiny of my own. For a start vetting was required of the then Director Dr Martin Johnson, with the letters; BD PhD MSc FRSA after his name. Researching FRSA, and in some doubt, I contacted the Royal Society of Arts to enquire if this was an award made by them. They advised it was, but couldn't state the specifics of what it was for; although I got the impression it concerned contributions for general social good. At the time on the TTUK website Dr Martin Johnson's credentials listed; BD and PhD. Again my research didn't manage to 100% decipher but does not appear to be remotely medical. The distinct impression it left me with, was a qualification for a Bachelor of Divinity following a phone call to a university that runs courses with relevant certification. If this is indeed the case then such background and accreditation may be highly valid, and exceedingly applicable to those seeking an appointment to or by an Archbishop. However it does not pertain to, or cut the mustard if acting as a voice of authority, and canon of information on medical, biological and scientific matters pertaining to the harms of *Thalidomide* on the unborn.

Concerns are not so much about any given individual per se or the level of sincerity of that individual, but wider underlying sub-issues. That is regardless of one person whoever they may be and however reasonable a person they are, it is totally unacceptable a person is or can be in an office/ position to advise erroneous facts as valid information at such an emphatic level to the medical world; and yet remain beyond reproach. It leads to a very obvious question. Where else are prefixes being used of Dr. that however unintentional, implies a medical status and authority that cannot be challenged whilst suppressing objectivity and blocking transparency, in the past, present or in the future.

Over the 2000's I picked up on ever more dubious spin presented on and in national media by TTUK, as an erroneous narrative was bolstered. The tone and tenor was in line with shoring up the implied inaccurate account. A total ban in 1961 was stressed more than the previously referred date of 1962 falsely implying immediately after not a single tablet was left available anywhere. In addition ongoing bogus claims of only a limited *"9 Week Sensitive Period"*, continued to be yet further underscored.

Perhaps if one takes 'the drug companies/ corporate/ establishment shilling, then maybe however indirectly this leads to toeing the line and promoting their cause based on their bias agenda using their misinformation? Do senior positions within TTUK and other settlement entities come with a poisoned chalice? That is an unspoken subtext to have to cover the backs of big corporation's flawed positions, and errant government failings and practices?

At the same time it is my expectation both Dr Martin Johnson and the *Thalidomide* Trust UK will over years have acted for the good of some people harmed by *Thalidomide*, especially a number impacted more extensively. Whilst this is clearly commendable, it must not to be confused or conflated with correctly asserting cases that were or were not caused by *Thalidomide* or extent of harm; and much less still for the organisation, position and office to impede open mindedness and transparency in a belligerent and unhelpful manner.

Any *Thalidomide* survivor acknowledged and supported by any settlement organisation is a good thing and much to be commended. However this needs to be extended wider to encompass all *Thalidomide* survivors globally regardless of; the extent of harm and time frame of pregnancy, or the year when exposure occurred, or place where the drug was taken. It is essential both the public and professions are made fully aware of the entire transparent picture of all the potential harms of *Thalidomide* (and its analogues), plus how they have been misadvised for decades. It is wrong to continue to have the real full account air-brushed into misleading sanitized sound bite type presentations for over 50 years by protected untouchable quasi public bodies.

Around 2009 with the lack of constructive input or any support from the TTUK, I sought new lines of enquiry and other potential angles to explore some *Thalidomide* issues. This however only resulted in stumbling upon something perhaps even more troubling.

Contergan was not sold in the UK, but was produced by Grünenthal as their original market brand of *Thalidomide,* for Germany and elsewhere. On approaching an entity appearing to be independent calling itself something like; Contergan International, I was both taken aback and unsettled when Dr Martin Johnson, the Director of TTUK made the response for Contergan International (or whatever it was called); unsurprisingly however only the same old spun propaganda and misinformation was forthcoming.

The feeling this left me with was even more disconcerting, as it suggested the same people are entwined in a unified on message approach presenting as independent, but really all singing from the same song sheet of overarching interests.

How this has come about and where the links of power stem from will be considered in further chapters. The Machiavellian and power orientated construct I sensed operating in the back ground, appeared to be silently guarding an inner circuit of hush out of sight, and beyond all radars.

This only raises further and more serious questions. Why are all parties interwoven? What then has been the real purpose, and real role of all the official *Thalidomide* organisations over the years? Who and where did this power originate? Equally as important, where does it reside today? Further related questions include; why and how have they got away with such poor practice over the last 50 years? It appears they have collectively been a law unto themselves. Or protected by governments? Perhaps the same thing, but either way it needs to be challenged and reversed.

A Grünenthal correspondence sent on the same day in late 1961 to the Drug Commission of the German Medical Association; expressed the reason for "withdrawal" of *Thalidomide* was due to media meddling that had overridden scientific evidence to misguide public opinion, not due to a problem with *Thalidomide* [2, p103-p104]. Besides the alleged scientific meddling being completely deluded and wrong in its entirety, it also demonstrates Grünenthal was not remotely in any way making a compelling safety alert or public health warning; but instead continued to proclaim an erroneous position and denial of any *Thalidomide* risks. It appears settlement entities continued to be subjugated to similar errant perspectives and stand points for the following 5 decades.

The above mentioned correspondence made by Grünenthal is microcosmic of all *Thalidomide* drug

Loose ends and unknown lengths of string

companies' cosmetic posture, and indicates at no point
has there been a real problem solving approach. Instead
it appears a highly slick form of behind the scenes arm-
twisting and troubleshooting to facilitate shutting down
of all legitimate debate and enquiry, even before any has
even been allowed to start. Over the years how many other
people trying to speak up for wider transparency on one
aspect or another concerning *Thalidomide* harms, have
been silenced from behind the scenes one at a time, before
they gain wider attention?

The numbers of people harmed and impaired by
Thalidomide and still not recognised is probably like how
long is a piece of string? For certain many other people will

have been harmed because *Thalidomide* was consumed after 9 weeks in pregnancy for a wide range of different reasons, both pre and post 1962 on "withdrawal" from the wholesaler. However individuals and affects inflicted on them are not acknowledged on any official figures, due to flawed recognition criteria. Thus an array and very wide spectrum of different types of harms and negative *Thalidomide* impacts have not ever been accounted for. Many of these people would not even be aware an impairment or health complication etc was the result of *Thalidomide* exposure, as will become more evident in further chapters of this book.

Over the first decade of the 2000's, it became apparent to me much had been screened out. It also became clear a great deal must have been spent for the *Thalidomide* establishment to continue to prop up errant presentations projected thus far for over 50 years. All the more reason to get hold of some loose ends and give a good tug, as the myths and fallacies perpetuated are long overdue to be publically undone. Going forward I realised to counter all of this, would be a process of joining up unseen dots...

"Success isn't measured by what you achieve, its measured by what obstacles you overcome." [3]

Ethan Hawke

10

A Phone Call for Help out of a National Park

On the Distaval/ *Thalidomide* trail between 2008 and 2010 there was a wider transition. During these years I had times of living near the edge of the Peak District National Park, so would go walking or cycling as often as possible. As a safety precaution I would take a mobile phone when venturing out into the Park. However signal was often unreliable, and hence if making a planned phone call I would invariably seek out one of the few remaining old fashioned red Telephone boxes. One classic design with a continuing appeal was the most widespread, created by Giles Gilbert

The next stage of an unpredictable journey

Scott in 1935, and then installed up to 1968 [1].

National Parks in the UK were established in 1949 by an Act of Parliament; to provide recreational opportunities for the public, and to preserve and enhance areas of outstanding natural beauty. The Peak District with its rugged moorland scenery, stretching from around Derby to the Manchester area was amongst the first designated UK National Parks in 1951; together with the Lake District, Snowdonia and Dartmoor [2].

On the Distaval/*Thalidomide* trail phone calls in the Peak District were prompted following some serendipity of a library visit, and noticing An Atlas of Foetal and Embryonic Development, by Marjorie J England (1973) [3]. Ironic, but the front cover picture has the photograph of a 16 week foetus, and this instantly caught my eye. Fine tuning into the proportions, I stood there stunned as it was clear the 16 week foetus had precisely the same physical proportions as me, including an identical ear position. My eye-to-ear line being presented in relation to a doctor's comments to me a few years earlier. By 2008 with some greater bioindicator awareness, it was exactly as I had expected, although at that point in time I was not aware of the full extent of inter-related issues revealed in future chapters.

Marjorie J England's book An Atlas of Foetal and Embryonic Development was produced in the early 1970's suggesting research went back to the 1960's, and was most likely influenced by *Thalidomide* events. It was produced with medical links to Leicester Hospitals I attended as an 8 year old boy, within only a couple of years after the first publication. See Chapter 3 Growing Concerns.

By simply observing Marjorie England's text book it showed my development had been universally impacted at 16 weeks, leaving my proportions effectively freeze-framed at this stage. Future findings in another text book by Marjorie England and Jennifer Wakely [4, p22-p25] provides unambiguous photographic evidence relevant specific parts of my brain would not have developed during and beyond 16 weeks.

At a red telephone box in the Peak District National Park on a dull indifferent late autumn day in 2008, the quest to overturn decades of Distaval/*Thalidomide* misinformation began in earnest. The telephone box had probably stood there from the 1960's perhaps since my journey began, and was avidly malting its layers of faded and weathered red paint. Once inside the telephone box the blunt northern wind abated, and I got out a handwritten list of places to call. The UK National Pharmacy Association was the first, to enquire of records of the drug dating back to the 1960's, but it soon became apparent they had nothing. Several other organisations and bodies were contacted, but they too offered no more. More contacts on the list included an NHS trust in the relevant East Anglia area, but these only led to more contacts to be followed up later.

Lastly was the telephone number of a local pharmacy in the small market town where my mother lived when she was pregnant with me. The pharmacy of that era went years ago, and the present store belonged to a contemporary national chain. They informed me UK pharmacy data had been computerised in the early 1980's, and all paper records would have long gone. Then advised the old G.P. surgery with its pharmacy thing no longer existed either, and this was before even knowing it was more accurately described as the G.P. dispensary.

A metaphor for the way ahead was more like free

climbing a sheer rock face in the National Park. Over future weeks and months more telephone calls were made from various telephone boxes whilst out cycling or walking. Calls included seeking information on my own medical records from the years of attending hospital clinics in childhood, concerning my reduced stature; but these records too had gone years earlier, most likely around the mid 1990's. My G.P. records had also been destroyed, losing all childhood and early adulthood entries. It was surprising to learn after a gap of about 6 years between visits, a surgery could destroy all records without a trace, or without retaining a summary and not even informing the person concerned.

Step by step more and more national and regulatory bodies, and various other organisations, were contacted and crossed off an ever expanded list. I even tried to contact some celeb' doctors and journalists; but mostly they never even replied.

Together with other things in life, it was soon over a year since my first phone call out of a red telephone box, but things hadn't really got very far. Despite a lot of people and places having been contacted, and there was also the sense time was ticking by but not much had provided in the way of answers.

On route at times chance reminders would reignite my efforts and spur me on. One such example was a display at the entrance of a library in the peak district on local community policing over the preceding 50 years. Exhibits included early versions of walky-talky radios, and old fashioned uniforms, plus a small note book tucked to one side. It had been hand written in date order. Commencing January through to February, and then on to the end of March 1966. On noticing this I couldn't help but imagine the person making diary notes in the same era my mother was taking Distaval/*Thalidomide* tablets. Each of the entries for March felt like a metaphoric representation, and it prompted me to re-engage from new angles on the Distaval/*Thalidomide* trail. The local library got hold of a number of 1960's annual Medical Directories, borrowed on loan from the main national British Library store. The doctors' information was of real interest and provided some extra insights here and there, again ruling things out as much as ruling things in. Although some information and leads from 2008 and 2009 did not become clear until later in the summer of 2011.

National records of doctors for 1965 showed at the old 1960's East Anglia G.P. surgery, there had been a Dr H. as my father had suggested. Although of more interest to me was a Dr. G. Fr. whom my mother had referred to, although his first name was not Gordon, but George as my father had recalled. Another curious anomaly was Dr. G. Fr. clearly was not as young as my mother had indicted, but then sometimes people look younger than they really are, and stay looking that way for years. It also transpired Dr. G. Fr. had passed away when I was about twelve years old, only days before it was most likely confirmed by the consultant to Distaval/*Thalidomide* had reduced my height. See Chapter 3 Growing Concerns.

After 2010 I no longer lived anywhere near the Peak District National Park, and consequently was no longer visiting its red telephone boxes to make further phone calls on the Distaval/*Thalidomide* trail. Nonetheless in later times initial ground work generated new leads in more serendipitous ways. One example was for a contact at a history exhibition in a relevant East Anglia location. By then I knew Dr G. Fr. had passed away years earlier, and the surgery in question with the pharmacy-dispensary had long gone. Yet driving over and physically meeting people might offer new insights into the dispensary at the old surgery, and just maybe someone could be found who recalled something...or even had worked there?

It was a bit of a long shot, but all the same I gave up a day and went to see what could be discovered. It turned out its general theme was agriculture and the contribution made by WW2 Land Girls'. Whilst it didn't take things further forward on the Distaval/*Thalidomide* trail it was of some interest, as my great aunt Nell had been a Land Girl in the 1940's. Growing up I had always liked my great aunt for her impish sense of humour and for growing grapes in her sun lounge. My uncle Bill whom she was married to would make wine out of the grapes, and used to steam clean his Morris Marina 1.7.L. engine. Another slight irony was I had come to believe my late great aunt Nell was probably the only person my mother had ever really confided in concerning Distaval/ *Thalidomide*. My reasoning is based on a number of factors, including how my great aunt Nell had come up to stay with my mother after I was born, to support her while suffering some post natal blues.

All the same none of this helped the Distaval/ *Thalidomide* trail in the 2000's. On the off chance late in the day, I asked around whether anyone present knew of connections for a Dr G Fr.? Or if there was anyone who had worked in the pharmacy thing at the GP surgery, or even the pharmacy in town; but nobody present offered anything new.

The steady drive back home was in the cool evening air that generated an inversion effect, creating a misty haze over the surrounding fields and countryside, where only parts of hedges and tops of trees jutted through. It made me contemplate the metaphor of, how much of the

Paul Whymark Photograpahy ©

A land of part concealing mists

Distaval/*Thalidomide* trail information had already quietly drifted off and become lost in the mists of time. As some no doubt had wanted, and would still wish to continue.

Out of the whole day and an around trip of over 300 miles (480Km) only one possible, but not very specific, new lead had been gained. Even this was only vague, from a person who might provide a contact for someone else? On arriving home I was tired, and my thoughts were it had been a nice day out, but it wasn't worth driving back over again. Quietly I put the new contact details into a desk draw, and before long it too had drifted from my consciousness as the days and weeks slipped by.

During my second year with the Field Studies Council in 2009 I had tried to come out more publically concerning Distaval/ *Thalidomide* exposure at weeks 16 to 20 of my gestation, and the consequences in me. In all cases trying to share this information with both remaining immediate family (and some relevant doctors in that era of my life)

it went down like the proverbial lead parachute. My
remaining family naively approached the *Thalidomide*
Trust UK (TTUK), and were erroneously advised it wasn't
possible for any harm to have occurred at 16 weeks in
pregnancy. TTUK also denied Distaval/*Thalidomide* caused
any affects or damage on the unborn beyond the mythical
so called limited 9 week sensitive period. To make things
more difficult TTUK used the slimy spun line of only a
rare bathroom cabinet Incident may have occurred up to
one year to 18 months, post 1962. After such time TTUK
emphatically, but inaccurately stated it was impossible
to be given or obtain *Thalidomide* in early 1966. All the
above is corporate spun P.R., and at best myopic ignorant
humbug, if not potentially far more cynical. It was not
only possible but inevitable, and most likely the drug was
obtained and used on countless occasions.

There was a significant reduction of new cases of
the stereo type *Thalidomide* babies due to reduction in
general use for morning sickness during the first 9 weeks
post 1962 to 1963. However that would not be the entire
account from a number of perspectives. For a start no
satisfactory recall was ever made, leaving significant stocks
of *Thalidomide* to exist without anybody knowing even
approximately the number of tablets out there in various
different guises. Add to the mix there were no public
safety campaigns warning of risks from existing stocks.
On top of these inadequacies, zero clear objective and
explicit warnings existed or were issued for the risks in
later pregnancy, and remarkably nor has there been to the
present day.

In the mid 1960's naive assumptions were **all** based on
the sham accounts and flawed conclusions, derived from
no more than only two phoney medical publications. One

was; *"The Trial of Thalidomide in Insomnia Associated with the Third Trimester"* published in the *American Journal of Obstetrics and Gynaecology* in 1961 under the name of Dr Ray Nulsen. It made a rambling conclusion claiming; *Thalidomide* is a safe and effective sleep-inducing agent, and safe for use in late pregnancy. These errant safety claims were based on unethical human experiments that were not even satisfactorily observed or concluded, then written up in a flawed testimonial contribution [5, p44]. Record keeping for the study was woefully inadequate, defective and without details, but the bad practice didn't end there, as Nulsen's paper was in fact drafted by Dr Pogge; the Director of Medical Research at Richardson-Merrell Inc., working with Grünenthal to promote *Thalidomide* in the US and Canada [5, p44] [6, p121-p124] [7, p78]. Yet these facts did not come out for another 15 years into the mid 1970's. Consequently medical professionals and the public would have been completely unaware claims for safety in later pregnancy, in the paper fronted by Dr Nulsen's name were and remained bogus. Dr Kelsey of the FDA [6, p121-p130], stated she would never have allowed *Thalidomide* to be used in pregnancy until evidence concluded it was safe for the entire full term of pregnancy.

The second misleading scientific claims came from twisting the facts in another article by Dr Augustin Peter Blasiu published May 2nd 1958 in *Medizinische Klinik.* *Thalidomide* was given by Dr Blasiu and colleagues to women who had already given birth and were nursing their babies. But the article derived from this episode had a misleading undercurrent, and implied safety had been observed for pregnant women. There was no mention of pregnant women being given the drug and Dr Blasui would not ever have done so, as he had long held a basic rule to never give any sleeping pills or tranquilizers to any pregnant women[8, p68-p70]. However this didn't stop Grünenthal selecting extracts of the article produced by Dr Blasui, and using them to imply *Thalidomide* was safe for use in pregnancy; and then disseminating these errant claims to 40,245 doctors [8, p68-p70]. The latter indicates the scale of the difficulty to contradict *Thalidomide* safety, as for years doctors had been sold *"complete safety"* and *"atoxity"*.

Despite these extracted claims being false and unsubstantiated, after *Thalidomide* was "withdrawn" from the wholesale market such assertions continued to live on and remained unchallenged in 1966. Even today over 50 years on it seems remarkable, but few if any in the medical profession seem really prepared to confront and challenge false safety claims within the first 9 weeks, let alone others in later weeks.

Thalidomide was marketed under around 37 different brand names, and for a wide range of different purposes [5, p16]. Generally *Thalidomide* was recommended for all of the following aliments during the 1960's; – colds/ flue, a daytime hypnotic, a sleeping pill, an anti anxiety or antidepressant/ emotional instability/ anti stress, epilepsy, migraine, back pain, a general pick up, calming for dental procedures, kidney disease, marital discord, functional bowel distress, abdominal pain [5, p41], and clearly anything else sub clinical. The Sunday Times once described claims for the drug as; *"If Thalidomide was not an elixir to cure all ills of mankind (humankind), then it was certainly intended to make them incomparably easier to bear."* [5, p41]

Following "withdrawal" from issuing any new *Thalidomide* product onto the market, and a general reduction of *Thalidomide* use in the first 9 weeks of pregnancy; it is not difficult to see and appreciate how it continued to be taken in one guise or another by women who happened to be pregnant on any day(s) in any of the remaining 31 weeks of pregnancy.

The only information to the public or professionals hinting at risks from *Thalidomide* related to a narrative of a mysterious potential during only the first 9 weeks. But even here the drug companies communicated they didn't believe this. In the UK public notification to "withdrawal" from new sales into the market was presented in the BMJ 2nd December 1961. Distillers Company Ltd stated; *"reports have been received from two overseas sources possibly associating thalidomide* ("distaval") *with harmful effects on the foetus in early pregnancy. Although the evidence on which these reports are based is circumstantial and there have been no reports arising in Great Britain, either clinically or pharmacologically we feel we have to withdraw the drug from the market immediately pending further investigation"* [9]. Following this they did not satisfactorily investigate further, but if anything shut down deeper investigation.

If that wasn't way too little in terms of warnings, the "withdrawal" notice itself implied there was no reason for concern either pharmacologically or clinically, i.e. disbelief and denial. In the same edition of the BMJ surrounding articles gave glowing support and admiration in general for *Thalidomide*. One talked of how non-barbiturate medication avoided dangers and therefore any drug that could avoid this must be a good thing. At the time this was tantamount to suggesting Distaval/ *Thalidomide*, but without directly naming the drug or saying so.

No credible follow up on testing for use in later pregnancy was ever made let alone communicated to either the public or the medical profession, and inevitably contributed to my mother being given Distaval/ *Thalidomide* in early 1966.

TTUK's misinformation around 2009 and after was enough for my family, medics, and others to conclude the establishment had to be right; based on no more than the premise, because the establishment couldn't ever be wrong, apparently. Hence thereafter all discussion effectively was ended, even though in reality no discussion had ever really started. It very much appeared as though the *Thalidomide* establishment wanted silence, and above all those with a legitimate voice to be kept silent. Regardless of any such unjustified wishes *"16 Weeks and Everything After..."*© will not ever be going silently, not now or any time in the future.

Again it felt belittling as if TTUK were mocking from a far my efforts to establish and publicise the facts, perceiving their corporate backed and establishment might was untouchable, and would continue to subjugate the medical profession, and therefore the public. Any such implication Distaval/*Thalidomide* could be trivialized to a level of Bathroom Cabinet Incident is wrong in the extreme, and needs to be challenged. Not least as for the person concerned impairments and negative impacts regardless of level or extent, last their whole entire lifetime. Not to mention the fact any and all *Thalidomide* harms were and are a total violation on a human life, whenever, however, and wherever they took place.

Ultimately the unsound advice and defective accounts of the *Thalidomide* establishment doesn't change the real facts from being quite different to those presented over the last 50+ years. Residual inaccuracies that became fossilized in tablets of stone as the official doctrine, distracted people from looking in the right places, and much less asking the right questions. Thus preventing anyone ever doubting, and even less ever challenging or confronting the flawed residual misinformation, and unseen agenda's of *Thalidomide*'s self appointed authority.

By 2011 my investigation no longer only concerned the harm Distaval/*Thalidomide* caused me, but in addition a wider untold societal account. During the time I had made phone calls from the red telephone boxes in the North of England, it became obvious I could not leave things as they were, and as they had been for decades. The method of approach uses daylight to dismantle all misleading misinformation constructs, piece by piece. *"16 Weeks and Everything After..."*© has achieved all of this, and probably in ways even inconceivable to the ever vigilant and watchful eye of the *Thalidomide* establishment.

Piecing together all the aspects of the Distaval/*Thalidomide* picture was like a huge and complex jigsaw.

Some jigsaw puzzles require a bit of extra perseverance

Metaphorically it was like a considerable sky and ocean puzzle cut into many pieces, presenting in endless different shades of subtle hues from blue to white. All the pieces are there, they always were; although they didn't necessarily go together quite as one might initially anticipate. Nonetheless the pieces have always been there, and do indeed fit and match perfectly, revealing a quite different picture than has been officially presented thus far.

Phone boxes are becoming an ever rarer sight, with total ubiquity of mobile and smart phones but are being used in a number of creative ways from green houses for pot plants, to micro libraries of used books [10]. They have been sold all over the world, from China to Russia, but the most popular destination for used Telephone boxes continues to be the UK. In London old Telephone boxes have been used as mobile phone-charging points, powered by solar panels on the roof. Many people would like to see them preserved, and perhaps on occasions this could radically be extended to even being used as a telephone

In a National Park self reliance is often the only option

box? At home as much in the city as on some remote hillside, somehow they still hold something of a reassuring presence, as if things in life can all work out in the end.

As I put the telephone handset down on that first telephone call, something inside of me had irreversibly changed, and there would be no turning back. The unmasking of the airbrushed historical account concerning Distaval/*Thalidomide* had unwittingly been assisted on its way, by a phone call for help out of a National Park.

'Great oaks from little acorns grow" [11]

English Proverb

11

Notable Connections
at Aberdeen

At times contradictions from official information created a fog of impasse. However obstacles hindering transparency were overcome, as significant pieces of the jigsaw on the Distaval/ *Thalidomide* trail gradually began to emerge and fall into place.

Sharing rented accommodation with East Europeans led to impromptu English language support that would result in the suggestion, *"You should be an English teacher"*. With no work, and no other prospects on the horizon in 2011, life was continuing on an unpleasant downward spiral, and

All roads (and rail tracks) lead to Aberdeen

I began to wonder if it could somehow offer a way forward. Even if only as a temporary option while things picked up. My abilities and aptitudes were not up to even getting through a PGCE and therefore mainstream education would not have been a starter. However working abroad Teaching English as a Second Language (TESOL), particularly to adults as improving business English is an alternative.

Life is no dress rehearsal, so during January 2012 I went to Florence in Italy for a month TESOL certificate. All over Florence there are endless amazing works of art, more than I could take in, but provided a greater appreciation of the Renaissance. There must have been an army of people with immense talent, and not only the genius of Michelangelo and Leonardo D' Vinci et al. Probably why the Italians continue to be particularly good at creating beautiful and artesian things from clothing to cars, bicycles, wine and just about everything else.

Allegory of Spring by Sandro Botticelli at the Uffizi Gallery, has an enigmatic beauty and energy on viewing difficult to describe, but sort of felt like being put into a trance. It is still worth seeing on the internet or in a book, but its real power is in real life. Peter Ustinov said, *"If Botticelli were alive today he'd be working for Vogue"* [1].

The River Arno is the most significant river in Tuscany and just past Florence it travels west out to the sea, about 7 ½ miles (12km) away a little beyond Pisa; home of the leaning tower. The River Arno starts its journey way back in the Apennine Mountains about 150miles (241km) away, and picks up waters from the north flowing River Elsa and south flowing River Sieve. In late summer and early autumn of 1966 it swelled larger than it had for centuries [2] creating the historic 1966 flood. This damaged priceless pieces of art and in some cases irrevocably, but it only elicited and produced great artistic skills in renovation. Today water levels have constant monitoring, assisted by the use of computers and technology [2], but The Great Flood of 1966 left its mark, culturally, and physically all over Florence including high water marks.

On daily seeing these high water marks, it began to generate a subliminal concept in my thinking, of how only a few months earlier in 1966 I too had become an unreported 'high water mark' of exposure to Distaval/ *Thalidomide*. Perhaps following *"16 Weeks and Everything After..."*© one day they'll put a stone plaque on a wall, for the high watermark' of exposure to Distaval/ *Thalidomide*?

Either way the constant reminder of high water marks resulted in me giving greater contemplation to Italy's history of *Thalidomide*, something up to then I had not previously considered to any real extent. In the TESOL month there was no time to work on the Distaval/*Thalidomide* trail.

16 W.&E.A. Photo - Art © Photo: Tracy Scuderi

High water marks tell of unimaginable occurrences
(Photography support: Tracy Scuderi)

However on returning to the UK I explored more of Italy's experience of *Thalidomide*, and even contacted an Italian *Thalidomide* survivor. Advice from Italy stated the brand of *Thalidomide* was Contergan, and had been in use up to 1965 and most likely beyond, over three years after the supposed "withdrawal" of Contergan in Germany. In all probability *Thalidomide* was used beyond this time as controls and safeguards were limited and less enforced, especially perhaps in rural areas. In Italy as in other countries there was a lack of advice to use not during later pregnancy, hence only the implied contrary. The *Thalidomide* drug companies had used two reports claiming safety in later pregnancy. Both were adapted to fit inaccurate accounts and based on false constructs, then misused to claim safety during in pregnancy when the data did not show this, or even seek to find it [3, p121-p130] [4, p78] [5, p68-p70].

It appears Italy got the same carefully choreographed P.R rinse that focused on "withdrawal" from the wholesale market, as did Ireland and the UK. Worse still on US Television in 1965 Grünenthal propaganda continued to claim *Thalidomide* was completely safe, implying all stages of pregnancy. This was over three years after the "withdrawal" from the wholesaler [3, p176]. Grünenthal continued publishing propaganda in different Newspapers and Journals of claims there were no risks from use *Thalidomide* in pregnancy in 1966 during February to late May. These articles cited professionals such as noted scientists who either questioned validity of claims against *Thalidomide*, or proposed alternative theories for the cause of malformations of babies [3, p232-p235]. Ironic if not sardonic but the above time window included weeks 16 to 20 of my foetal development when my mother took Distaval/ *Thalidomide* in March of that same year.

In the UK, Distillers Company Bio-chemicals Ltd also did nothing for transparency. Duke, Hellman and Tucker proposed *Thalidomide* inhibited rejection of transplanted tissue due to suppressing immunological responses [3, p164-p166]. Duke, Hellman and Tucker's misguided interpretation of results implied *Thalidomide* was not causing the malformations and harms in babies, but instead prevented otherwise self aborting embryos. This was not the case, but Grünenthal immediately seized on this distracting information, and used it to yet again to bolster continued bogus claims of *Thalidomide* complete safety. Only a matter of a few weeks after Duke, Hellman and Tucker seminars in London suggesting *Thalidomide* safety, my mother became pregnant with me.

During spring 2012 I sought more supporting evidence using genetic testing to confirm there were no other medical reasons for my reduced limb size, and ear positions etc. Foetal Alcohol Syndrome (F.A.S.) was immediately eliminated because my mother was effectively a tea-total her whole life. Plus affects in me are not representative of F.A.S., and pre-existing development in me before 16 weeks is unaffected. There was no real reason to consider genetics, yet it could be seen as in leave no stone unturned territory, and would be helpful to convince a sometimes sceptical and in denial medical profession of the 2000's.

The Idea had arisen around 2010 from another exchange with the *Thalidomide* Trust UK (TTUK) that again for me felt condescending, communicating they were not a campaign group and had no interest in changing the status quo. It was around the time when TTUK were conversing with Gordon Brown's Government for improved settlements for recognised (but not the ignored unrecognised) *Thalidomide* survivors. TTUK insisted to even consider my impossible situation, as they put it, would at least require genetic testing to rule out my physical features weren't due to any type of inherited medical condition. Initially TTUK's response stalled me and some months passed, perhaps even over a year, but in 2011 I decided to do just that and approached my G.P.

Some in the medical profession have been defensive and close minded on the issue, but my G.P.'s response was refreshingly open-minded and constructive. They swiftly arranged the required genetics testing and offered comments on the lines of, *"Medicine can always learn new things"*, and in an unbiased and non-judgemental way added, *"Whatever the outcome it might produce something interesting"*. Despite the positive start, some time passed without hearing anything further. At first I let more time drift, and then a bit more, but it began to feel strange there was nothing forthcoming, as if something had got lost in the post.

Contacting the surgery, I discovered they had only recently received a return correspondence, and this had declined all genetic tests. It seemed illogical but my G.P. surgery advised they would forward me the correspondence sent by the genetic testing centre that I then scanned into a pdf.

On reading the April 2011 letter from the genetic testing centre it instantly raised some serious *'red flags'*, as there were the unattractive hall marks of coded denials supplied by the *Thalidomide* Trust UK. The letter declining genetics tests made the false and counterfeit assertion it was not possible for me to have been exposed to Distaval/ *Thalidomide*. They stated disbelief Distaval/*Thalidomide* could be obtained in 1966, unless as they put it my mother, *"had kept a supply of tablets for 3–5 years after it was discontinued in the UK"*. Slime, was a word that came to my mind, although there were also a number of others. The additional bogus claim made concerned the errant so called critical/ sensitive gestational period for causing abnormality. Stated as between 34 to 50 days after LMP (last menstrual period), i.e. (4 weeks and 6 days through to 7 weeks and 1 day).

The above is no more than misinformation propaganda, i.e. the political not the real medical interpretations. Hard evidence against this was irrefutably in the public domain by 2011, if not many years and decades earlier. The wider public probably did not notice as media focus was on the economic crisis, and to some extent a war with dubious legality. However in reality it does not wash for the *Thalidomide* Trust UK to posture or pretend of not knowing in 2011. In 2009 medical science by Dr Neil Vargesson unambiguously demonstrated the harmful action of *Thalidomide* is (and always was) antiangiogenesis caused by unsettling vascular functioning [6]. In addition a number of top clinicians and scientists had previously been asserting the harmful action was in effect antiangiogenesis by vascular impairment for 30 to 40+ years by 2011. This means exposure to *Thalidomide* at any and all stages of pregnancy carries real risks of negative impacts and harm to the developing baby; i.e. for everyday of the first 9 weeks (the pre-embryonic and embryonic phase), including all the days not recognised but side stepped within the first 9 weeks, plus potentially every single day in all the remaining 31 weeks (the foetal phase) of pregnancy.

Throughout the 2011 correspondence from the genetic testing centre, ran the obnoxious P.R. spin of TTUK; the legacy settlement entity of Distillers Company Ltd. Hence it was no surprise to discover additional TTUK Website attachments. The style of slippery snake oil wording overtones conveyed a deluded superiority that felt distinctly creepy. It was presented in political with small *'p'* stock phrases of management speak. For example; *"Furthermore the period during pregnancy when the drug may have been used is too late to have caused any recognisable adverse effects of Thalidomide"*. Enclosed for further (miss-) information was a propaganda print out from the *Thalidomide* Trust UK website. In addition a TTUK complements slip was attached to the corner, with a scrawled handwritten, *"Contact; 01480 – 474074"*… *"Speak to Dr Johnson"*, (the then, Director of TTUK – N.B. an academic doctor not a medical one, and appearing to demonstrate considerable ignorance of the long indicated antiangiogenesis action of *Thalidomide*, and all the potential consequential affects on developing life including human foetal development).

This was not coming from the genetic testing institutions, but clearly vicarious TTUK falsehoods. It left me with a disturbing sense of being in a sinister underhand movie plot. But this wasn't a film during 2011, instead real life in the UK a supposed modern free democratic society, or so we are told? It showed a modus operandi to be very similar, to the bad practice undertaken by the drug companies and establishment five decades earlier. Such creepy behind the scenes Machiavellian misleading phrases would most likely have impressed 1960's Grünenthal Hench men, and Enoch Powell as Minster for Health in 1962, plus the main movers and shakers at Distillers Company Bio-chemicals Ltd. But it didn't impress me as it is not acceptable; hence it did not, nor will it deter me going forward.

Attempts to silence legitimate issues are way out of order, and must therefore never be accepted, but instead always challenged, and overturned. The above stated *'reasons'* for declining genetic testing in the correspondence to my G.P., were the very reasons why I was seeking to ensure the tests were obtained in the first place. That was, and is the very objective, i.e. to expose these inaccuracies and falsehoods for what they are, and always have been.

Morally the TTUK should have been proactively seeking to assist me to obtain the genetic tests, as it was TTUK that had stated a need for the tests in the first place. This was said to be to rule out other possible none *Thalidomide* causes for being effectively freeze framed for a life time at 16 weeks of gestation. At this point a new level of understanding descended on me, in relation to the dark forces my mother, and the consultant I saw would have been up against during my child hood hospital visits in the 1970's and 1980's.

It felt like nothing less than sabotage, by a long menacing stealthy arm reaching out from pools of darkness from within the shadows. Could this be a strategy of the liability holders Diageo, of the former Distillers Company Ltd in a joint agreement with the UK government, and also in cahoots with Grünenthal and the German Government?

Either way it appears for some, my work and endeavours for a more open, transparent and accurate account of the broader untold impacts and history of *Thalidomide* was getting too close for comfort. If you're beginning to wonder what other drugs and where else in big pharma, environmental or other issues this could be happening, then you're not the only one.

My G.P.'s practice had acted well on my behalf and done their best, but the system they were working with and were up against was distinctively less supportive. To ensure the genetic testing was obtained, I again took matters back into my own hands and doggedly refought an alternative route. It wasted another year, but finally I got an appointment with a child growth consultant. On arrival at the hospital outpatients it produced many strange feelings of Déjà Vous, from the subliminal feel of clinics I attended over thirty years earlier in Leicestershire. The consultant I saw in 2012 was a colleague of the other consultant, who had previously declined genetic testing based on flawed and erroneous misinformation from TTUK. Consequently for the first few minutes I had to battle past the indoctrinated propaganda of the *Thalidomide* establishment, and their false narrative and assumptions the medical profession has been saddled with for over five decades.

The consultant was a bit younger than me, perhaps 10 years or so, and he was well versed in modern protocol. Over the years I have noticed a notable generational gap exists on assumptions for health and safety, based on contemporary cultural norms. The consultant in 2012 didn't seem to grasp how in the 1960's, aspects of safety were not always adhered to, or compliance always necessarily as well enforced.

We talked about my ear-to-eye line position, and he agreed my visual appearance presented as expected for a 16 week foetus. Yet to my frustration I couldn't get him to go beyond assigning it to a box called unknown, as he put it. My request for a skull x-ray to evidence the 16 week foetal skull was declined on health and safety grounds, although I sensed it was as much about his disbelief. This was despite advising my skull x-ray would answer everything, and informing him I had seen it on two previous occasions; once around 1979, and for a second time only recently in 2011.

Things had gone round in circles, but introducing the height issue, my argument finally won through. Present in the room was a trainee who wasn't as yet so indoctrinated, and as a result was a bit more open minded. He looked in a questioning manor at the consultant who was keen to be thorough and professional all-round. The consultant asked the height of my parent's, but clearly wasn't expecting the answers I gave. On advising him my father's height is c. 5' 8½" (175 cm) and my mother's height was c. 5' 2" (159 cm), his instant reaction was to drop his pen; knowing even without glancing at his chart or table my answer was not possible for an adult male, i.e. literally off the scale at the low end.

He looked over at the trainee and then back to me, *"are you sure?"* he asked. My reply was; *"Yes, absolutely, in fact I have slightly underestimated, because in reality my mother was in fact more like 5' 2½" maybe even about 5' 3" a tiny bit taller than me...but we used to pretend we were the exact same height; and my father, well he was also if anything a bit taller; more like 5' 9", especially back in 1966"*. The consultant picked up his pen again, and triple checked the relevant data on his charts and tables. For male offspring the height range is contained within the formula; mother's height + fathers height + 5" (13cm): then divided by 2 = 'X' midway average most likely height. The range is then +/- from 'X' height by 4" (10cm) from 'X'.

Therefore for me 'X' would be 5' 2½" (159cm) + 5' 9" (175.5cm) + 5" (13cm) = 136½" (347.5cm): Next divided by 2 = 68¼"/ 5' 8¼" (173.25cm) as the midway and average height. The lowest possible genetic height for an adult male = 'X' 5' 8¼" (173.25cm) minus 4" (10cm) = 5'4¼" (163.25cm) i.e. from the height of my parents. N.B. the tallest is 6' 1¼" (184cm)

[For female offspring subtract 5" (13cm) instead of adding to the total parent height then find female 'X' followed by the same +/- 4" (10cm) range for max/min possible heights.]

Hence the amount of height below the minimum I am expected to be destined genetically from my parents height is at least 2" to 2½" (5.0cm to 6.5cm) below the lowest 1%tile; i.e. in practical terms not possible, without some genetic issue or harmful interference from Distaval/ *Thalidomide*. In real terms I have estimated based on the predictable height range of potential intended height is effectively over 30% less than the minimum, the average being 50% taller. Hence my real destined height would have been 5' 7" to 5' 9", i.e. 5" to 7" (12.5cm to 18cm") taller than my actual height post Distaval/ *Thalidomide* exposure.

The consultant measured my hands length and found them only just making the lowest 1%tile of the population in length, yet below the minimum possible for width. Nonetheless he again looked surprised when I advised my hands are smaller than my mothers were. It's my hunch that my hands would have been even smaller, and my feet likewise, if it were not for my wonderful grandfather (owner of the Morris Minor) on my mother's side. This is because his hands and feet were about the largest proportionally I have ever seen on anyone, and I have some of his genes. Yet even with this my overall cubit size is still below the minimum, and taking into account my hand span just about making the lowest 1%tile of the population of adult males.

Despite my hands being very small their contradictory proportionally larger size length is confirmed by human proportion used in art, as there are 10 human hand lengths to height. My hand length would put my height up to c. 170

cm (5' 7") about the height of both of my grandfathers; not c.158 cm (5' 2") my actual height. However of course this only represents growth of my hands to weeks 16 not fully developed revealing again I would have been taller, c. 5' 9" (175cm) like my father, or perhaps even taller still? After all the genetic potential for my height at the other end of the extreme 1% is 6' 1¼" (184cm); but not 6' 3¾" that is the equating reciprocal of my actual height.

My lack of stature compared to the minimum expected from my parents tipped the balance back in line with my argument. The consultant hesitantly looked back over at the trainee, who continued with a questioning and quizzical manor. The consultant then turned to me a bit vexed, and stated it was unusual, but there are some genetic conditions that could leave those types of presentations. Continuing, he said he had a medical duty to investigate, to rule out any such genetic conditions as there were no other obvious indicators. He warned of potential difficult news and explained the tests were to identify any genes for genetic explanations, e.g. some dysplasia type conditions, not that I had any concerns here. Next he took a sample of blood with great skill and care, such I was still waiting for the needle when he said *"all done"*, and stuck a plaster on my arm. Thanking him, I explained I would be away out of the country for a while, but looked forward to the results.

The rest of the year I went to Vietnam to work on TESOL and environmental projects' with a US not for profits organisation together in collaboration with a Vietnamese provider based in Hanoi. It was a great opportunity to meet an amazing people, and appreciate a civilization predating the Western world by millennia. In the UK it might sound unbelievable, but the only public swimming

Amazing Vietnamese skills and ingenuity

pool I managed to discover in Hanoi was closed when the weather fell to only +34° C, apparently because it was *"too cold"*. The heat with humidity was a bit on the high side during the summer, but explains why like the Italians, the Vietnamese also make some exceptionally good ice cream; and Vietnamese coconut is perfect for such conditions of sweltering humid heat, unless you have a nut allergy then there are other good options.

Arriving back to the UK in 2013, there was a bit of chasing for the genetic tests results, but the ground work had been done and the data followed not long after.

There are no genetic reasons or basis for my reduced stature, reduced arm/ cubit, leg size, or ear position, or brain impairments or anything else being freeze framed at the 16 week stage of foetal development; but instead exposure to the toxic teratogenic agent Distaval/

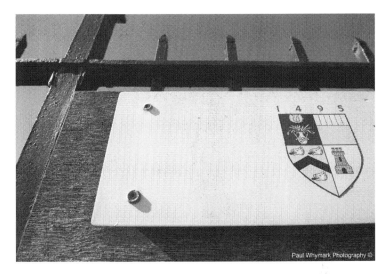

Science at Aberdeen indicated much wider Thalidomide harms have always existed

Thalidomide that negatively impaired all my development during weeks 16 to 20 of my mother's pregnancy.

There is however an over arching connection linking all my 16 week foetal biomarkers and it has nothing to do with genetic conditions, but instead what *"16 Weeks and Everything After..."* © refers to as the *"Aberdeen Connection"*. Science in 2009 by Dr Neil Vargesson at Aberdeen University definitively evidenced *Thalidomide*'s harmful action on the foetus and embryo is (and always was) antiangiogenesis [6]. Antiangiogenesis means, and does exactly what it says, on the side of tin/ bottle/ box/ packet etc; i.e. *"anti"* = against, opposed to, resistant, blocks, prevents;

"angio" = vascular system, blood vessels;

"genesis" = originates, beginning, start of, birth of, formation, creation

Thus, antiangiogenesis is in essence very simple and

straightforward; it concerns obstructing, stopping and preventing the development and formation of new blood supply. This action is sometimes referred to as blocking angiogenesis.

As a consequence this negative action on the vascular system prevents future development of all types of cells from successfully forming. This is especially the case for more delicate and smaller cells, e.g. brain cell formation.

At 16 weeks of foetal gestation, the brain and limbs are trying to complete all relevant stages of development, but the antiangiogenesis action of *Thalidomide* restricts blood supply and prevents the required development. As a consequence development is reduced and impaired, and cannot be fully completed thereafter. The antiangiogenesis action of *Thalidomide* means there is never a safe gestational time to be exposed to the drug, and destroys the myth and falsehood of only a limited *"9 week sensitive period"*. Aberdeen University studies were based on in vitro, i.e. not on real live developing human beings, for ethical reasons. Not that ethics remotely prevented Grünenthal and Distillers Company Bio-chemicals Ltd, et al, conducting about the largest ever unethical human drug experiment that I too am part of.

Finally the fight back against Grünenthal, Distillers Company Bio-chemicals Ltd et al, together with their arms length settlement bodies, cloaked in a dark sinister legacy of *Thalidomide* misinformation was now gaining ground and real impetus. The antiangiogenesis action of *Thalidomide* has the potential to harm developing babies at all stages of embryogenesis, providing significant connections at Aberdeen[6].

"Bureaucracy defends the status quo long past the time when the quo has lost its status" [7]

Laurence J. Peter

12

Life is Stranger than Fiction

It would sometimes almost feel like a competition to find the most obscure or unlikely Distaval/*Thalidomide* linked revelation. More than one event could be in contention for the title and phrase, life is stranger than fiction, if not perhaps the overall situation.

Willow trees are an often unconsidered national feature with some notable cultural links. Use in cricket bats offers properties of absorbing high impacts, yet provide enough resilience for batting cricket balls up to c.100mph/ 160 Kph, [1, p286]. An observable feature of willow trees are their long bendy branches, often by streams, becks and rivers, not surprising it has been used for many impact encountering purposes including ammunition hampers dropped from aircraft and for hot air balloon baskets [1, p186].

Willow bark and root nodules are rich in components of salicylic acid (aspirin), it's anti–inflammatory and analgesic properties has been used for reducing blood clots and as a preventative agent against thrombosis [2, p177-p178]. Aspirin is one of nature's oldest analgesics, originally obtained from willow (Salix) leaves and barks [1, p214].

Willow trees and willow bark might seem an unlikely place to start for a *'life's stranger than fiction'* scenario, but the connection was to provide the most remarkable sequence of events. One of my mother's saying would be, *"life's stranger than fiction"*, and sometimes add, *"You couldn't make it up"*. The funny thing is sometimes life really is stranger than fiction, to the point where it really couldn't be made up. When things like this happen it is sometimes also said, *"It could only happen in real life"*, i.e. the notion being it isn't possible to dream up such unpredictable and improbable situations.

Around 2002 I reopened an old wound/ scar from an operation 20 years earlier and as a result it left me with a minor hernia type injury. It took a further seven years to get resolved but finally the required operation was obtained, and went really well. Within 24 hours I was out and back at home, although the real recovery took much longer. Immediate post op' some opiate type pain killers were given to me, strong enough to produce effects of euphoria so much that against the nurses' wishes I had wanted to carry a full rucksack to the car, with hopes of going hiking.

For continued pain management some additional particularly strong prescription only painkillers were

Fiction is half predictable real life is not

supplied by the hospital. All the same I have never
liked taking anything unnecessarily and avoid any
pharmaceuticals including analgesics where ever possible.
That said when and where necessary I tend to go for
aspirin. Aspirin has had mixed medical perceptions and like
all medication has to be seen in a risk/ benefit ratio, and in
some cases may cause internal bleeding or other unwanted
side effects.

Aspirin originated from willow bark (Salix) and could
be seen as closer to a natural option, even though modern
versions are probably synthesised without so much as sight
of a willow leaf. At low dosage, aspirin has been linked
to prophylactic (preventative) action for heart disease to
cancers, and some view it as having the most advantageous
gains for people in their early 40's. At the time it related
to my stage in life, and therefore besides required pain
relief I had thought it might be the least bad painkiller to
take. However dosages for pain relieve and prophylactic
consumption differ, and may produce quite unlike bio
effects, so it is always a good idea to check with a medic
before self administering.

Recuperation after the operation made steady progress
for a couple of months, until encountering a setback on a
short walk to post a letter at a nearby post box. It was at
the end of a late winter afternoon, and it could have been
the gloom and lack of daylight, or maybe it was the gravel
on an unpredictable camber, but without warning I fell
crashing to the ground. Rolling on to the pavement over
the beaded gravel, I felt a depressing sinking sense of an
internal pull or tear. For a few minutes I lay there frozen,
contemplating whether to move or not. My real fear was
the operation would need repeating all over again. Very
gradually I got to my feet and slowly went home to phone

for medical support. Advice from the hospital was to undergo complete rest, and extend the taking of pain killers until healing was well underway.

Around mid May 2011 aside from the up's and downs of recovery from the operation, a new health concern had emerged in the form of an unsettling cough. All the usual herbal remedies like Echinacea had been tried with no effect, and I couldn't quite seem to shake it off. Increasingly it became difficult to ignore and the cough was strange because no obvious reasons could be thought of to explain or rationalize it, nor had I ever been a smoker either. Visiting my G.P. they offered good care and listened attentively. The doctor gave the issue some serious thought to try and work out a satisfactory diagnosis, yet there were aspects about the cough somewhat out of the ordinary and a bit of a concern. To be on the safe side I was promptly sent for a chest x–ray at a local and newly expanded hospital, with ultra modern up to date equipment, only about 3½ miles away.

The x-ray operative made the chest scan, and it presented on a brand new flat TV screen. The scan had nothing untoward and gave an all clear, but the x–ray only had covered up to the top of my chest, and it hadn't scanned the area where the cough was present. The x-ray operative and I discussed how the x-ray may not fully provide enough for an effective diagnosis. How the discussion evolved is no longer recalled but I agreed without any pressure, a single skull x–ray at the very lowest and safest dose possible was required. This ensured throat and neck area could be reviewed, and enabled assessing whether any issues presented in brain areas. Unsurprisingly at a sensible level of x–ray dose it was the least of any my concerns, given the potential outcome of missing something until it was too late. Whether the x-ray operator mentioned what would happen to these images I am less certain, but more recently have come to think the images would only be retained if needed, i.e. if they showed there was a problem or issue.

The procedure was over in seconds, and quickly I moved back to eagerly see the results arrive on the TV monitor. Gradually the computer uploaded the x–ray onto a large flat screen, and there it was much magnified in size, as a light green image set onto a dark background revealing every smallest detail.

Instantly I was struck by an unusual bone structure in the lower oblique aspect of my skull right behind the jaw bone. The x-ray operative seemed oblivious to this, but instead in line with their job requirements pointed out the completely clear areas in the soft tissues around my neck and head. *"Your all clear on this one...no problems there",* the operator said in an uplifting voice. Moving away they started filling out some admin and added with a gentle smile, *"Bet that's a relief"!* In reply I spoke only faintly, *"yeah...sure".* Nonetheless by then I had become completely distracted from why the x–ray had even been taken in the first place.

Now my head was in such a spin it was a struggle to get my thoughts and words together, stunned by what was on the TV screen. My only come back was, *"But what's that though?"* I said, pointing across the room to the x–ray on the large TV screen. Perched on the edge of the brand new thickly padded emerald green seat, I persisted, *"the coat hook and nail type bones".* The x–ray operative only half glanced up, from their admin task and understandably had no interest in looking beyond different coloured patches of soft tissue. In only a matter of fact way they replied, *"...*

just bones, they've shown through...that's all", reassuringly adding, *"Nothing to worry about...you're all clear, its good news".*

Shutting down the image they said it was ok to go, and advised they would contact my GP. *"Thanks"*, I said quietly. Even before I left the x–ray room the reality was I simply and absolutely knew that what I had just seen was effectively a 16 week foetal skull, regardless of not ever previously having researched foetal skulls of any gestational time frame. By 2011 my 16 week biomarker(s) radar ran real time continuously 24/7 in the background.

Walking out into the bright sunshine on that June day in 2011 I felt dazed and knocked off my stride. It was late morning around midday and it had become very warm, so I decided to go straight back home for some lunch, and more to the point something for rehydration. Walking back there was only one thing on my mind, and that was nothing to do with all that had been on my mind earlier the same morning, whilst walking in. Now all my mental energy focused on how I had just probably identified yet another 16 week foetal biomarker; and most likely a very significant, if not definitive one.

On internally describing the x–ray image, I started to sub vocalize the arbitrary thought of; *"it's like my head didn't develop in pregnancy"*. In that moment my walking speed reduced to hardly moving, and the traffic noise blurred into a single note, then a muffled silence. With ever smaller steps, I continued repeating the sub vocalized phrase; *"head didn't develop in pregnancy".* It was as if the physical steps were also psychological ones, as without warning I suddenly felt the need to physically draw breath. My walking had completely stopped by now and I was standing motionless, no longer really conscious of my immediate surroundings. Mentally more than half of me had already left 2011 and arrived back as a 12 year 10 month old boy in 1979. Suddenly I realised what the skull x–ray at a childhood hospital visit was all about. Effectively the consultant must have been looking for a 16 week foetal biomarker.

It was as if the sun's rays in 2011 were streaming down into the 1970's NHS hospital consulting room, through the gaps of the metal window blind. Back then x–rays were large analogue film sheets that were projected onto a wall mounted light box. I sat in the middle while the child growth consultant sat to the right and my mother to the left. On the wall in front there was an x-ray of my 12 to 13 year old skull was clearly displayed. *"Why are you giving me a head x–ray?"*, and *"What's that got to do with me being small?* I asked. The doctor seemed uncertain as to what he should say, and looked to my mother for a lead, who in return was equally unsure how to explain. Following a slightly confused and awkward silence, the doctor made the reply, *"The x-ray is to see if your head developed in pregnancy"*.

My incredulous disbelief at the illogical and feeble answer can still be remembered today, and I questioned it with; *"But you can see I have a head, so why do you need an x-ray?!?"* There were no satisfactory answers, despite protesting further, and eventually I gave up on trying for a better explanation.

Yet despite not knowing what was being looked for, and only with a boy's not an adult skull, I recalled enough of the salient features in my mind's eye. It conveyed the same fundamental bone structures I had seen earlier that morning in June 2011. During the intervening 30 odd years the above episode had slowly drifted from my memory, but in that moment it flew back at the speed of light and the

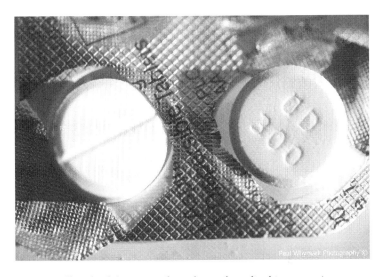

A willow bark legacy and unplanned medical interventions

weight of an x–ray machine.

Perhaps it was not surprising, but with all this bouncing around my head it resulted in a significant headache, especially combined with the heat and increasing dehydration on the 3½ mile walk home. Ironic, perhaps even sarcastically sardonic, but for the headache I ended up taking another 300mg of aspirin; the excess of which had been responsible for causing the cough that lead to the x–ray in the first place.

An extended chain of events over a number of years led to a remarkable find and insight, precipitated from the mild over consumption of a willow bark legacy, in the form of aspirin. The consequences led to discovering my skull was a 16 week foetal biomarker that otherwise may not have been revealed. You may at some level have experienced things unfolding a bit like this? But either way expect you can probably understand why it sometimes seems as life is stranger than fiction.

"You think you know what you're looking for until what you're looking for finds you."

Anon

13

A Bolt out of a Blue Sky

Malvern Hills rocks are made up from Pre-Cambrian granite estimated at c.600 million years old [1] [2, p10], and shaped as they are today around 200 to 250 million years ago. This is even further back in time than the Alps, Andes and Himalayas [1] hence the Malvern's provide a good place to gain perspective on things.

Summer skies over Worcestershire plane England

In 2010 and 2011 there was a second, if not a triple dip of recession yet to come, and my employment searches had been going round in circles that felt like ever decreasing ones. For both health gains and contemplation, it was time for a long walk on the Hills. Looking out over miles of countryside, I reflected on how life was still going to work out alright in the end, concluding all the setbacks were only part of the process of being human.

As John Lennon once said, *"life is what happens to you when you're busy making other plans"* [3, p155]. I have heard the same sentiments expressed as *"life is what happens between your plans",* and it is funny how often things work out this way. Following such walks in contact with nature, things always somehow feel clearer. On this particular occasion I came down from the hills with the notion based on the time management premise of: Important vs. Urgent, first do the things that are important and the urgent stuff that will have wait.

Free of much other mental clutter my focus and attention again turned to some accumulating in-tray tasks for the Distaval/*Thalidomide* trail. In particular was the contact at a library in the relevant East Anglia area where my parents and I had lived back in the 1960's. It had sat there for so long the exhibition it related to had been and gone, however the library advised me of another contact who was a local historian. My thoughts were it would probably only be another thing crossed off the list. In all the aspects of my personal journey on the Distaval/*Thalidomide* trail nothing seemed more random or unlikely for what happened next, even if it did evolve out of several stages.

On telephoning an East Anglia local historian it turned out he remembered the pharmacy thing, more accurately termed as the dispensary. I explained my family had lived there in the mid 1960's, and I was seeking general information to shed some light on types of drugs and medication it used to hold. He advised no records would exist this far out, and explained its purpose was mainly for people who could not travel in to the pharmacy in town. This confirmed something my mother had told me, and we got talking more generally. Thinking through possible ways to find out more, he suggested there was a person who might offer more insights. To my astonishment the individual he referred to was one of the doctors from back in the day. Although by 2011 I didn't think any of the doctors were still living. However he informed me Dr H. was still alive, although he had retired years ago. In much disbelief I questioned him again, but he assured me Dr H. was still around, and added he had only seen him in the last week.

It didn't seem possible, but I took down the telephone number for Dr H., although after I mulled over whether to phone him or not. In another leave no stone unturned moment I made a rough outline list of a few questions about the dispensary and whether Distaval/*Thalidomide* had been kept on the premises. In addition there was an extra question of no more than personal curiosity concerning a set of initials on part of my mother's medical records; on the off chance Dr H. might be able to shed some light on an aspect confirming some of Dr G. Fr.'s handwriting?

Mobile phone signal wasn't good, so I stood by the window with the phone held up high in one hand for better reception. My opening introduction to Dr H., first confirmed he was the doctor from the former surgery concerned, and he was still alive. This was reassuring on both sides, and especially for Dr H., because as Mark Twain once famously put it his demise was greatly exaggerated. The mutual reassurance produced quite a jovial conversation, and although I can't now put things in exact order, the salient aspects in substance and nature are outlined below.

Dr H., drew on his personal experience and explained like other doctors he had freely used Distaval/*Thalidomide* like a common analgesic e.g. aspirin, and often without any record keeping, particularly while he worked in hospitals during the early 1960's. It was bizarre but the way he was talking to me about Distaval/ *Thalidomide* conveyed a sense there had never really been a problem with the drug anyway. In some surprise I asked him if he could personally recall or had known of any problems, or difficult situations arising from its use. His comeback seemed very blasé, and he stated none that he could remember. Nonetheless my previous research had indicated claims of *Thalidomide* use apparently without adverse effects, even in the first 9 weeks. In addition I was aware the drug had been wrongly advocated use for later pregnancy, and so probed some more. Besides being a bit startled by the tone of his recollections I was also quite fascinated, especially thinking of the Australian promotion for use after weeks 12/ 13 in pregnancy. Was Dr H. saying Distaval/*Thalidomide* was used later on in pregnancy, after 12 weeks? The general impression from Dr H.'s responses was there was never a problem with Distaval/*Thalidomide* at any stage in pregnancy, and it felt like this was the overall vibe that came across no matter what angle I came from.

Against this I related it to the situation of my mother being given Distaval/*Thalidomide* at weeks 16 to 20. Again Dr H.'s response troubled me, as the conversation headed into an argument regarding the level of completion of foetal developmental at 16 weeks.

Dr. H. quoted a repeated verbatim one liner my mother would often say to me, when relaying what the doctor who prescribed her the drug advised. She would use both of the phrases below and therefore today I have difficulty in recalling which one of the two Dr H stated. However take your pick, as the intrinsic meaning remains the same. Like my mother, Dr. H may have also used both of the above verbatim phrases interchangeably. In addition although hard to convey exactly, Dr H. made the same sort of emphasis and intonation my mother would use when saying the phases below;

"The baby is fully developed all the organs are completed at weeks 16"...or...

"The organs are fully developed at weeks 16 and the baby is fully complete/d",

Somehow I managed to avoid a deep argument on levels of foetal development at weeks 16, but agreed to disagree; suggesting text books like those by Marjorie A England [4] [5, p22-p25] could be reviewed later if he wished, but either way not to worry, and moved on. For me the main focus was to get the most out of anything he remembered more specifically, despite being taken aback by some of his comments thus far.

Earlier on during our telephone conversation I had asked Dr H. if he could confirm some handwriting, on a couple or so entries on her medical records. It was only out of curiosity because if confirmed, the letters and handwriting might assist to try and decipher another bodged and muddied entry that could even be the prescription for Distaval/ *Thalidomide*.

The dilemma had concerned a small number of entries

written in extra fine biro, and these had some sort of squiggle after them appearing to be a set of initials, but were not easy to work out. Enlarging them on a computer indicated to me the squiggles could be *"G. F.".* If this was the case it signified they belonged to Dr G. Fr., unless there was another person with these initials?

Dr H. confirmed there was only one doctor who had worked at the surgery with these initials, and there had only been two other doctors besides him at the practice. Next he described the handwriting of Dr G. Fr.; saying he wrote in small handwriting, initialled things and used blue biro. This seemed to indicate the entries concerned were those of Dr G. Fr, but Dr H. agreed to confirm them if I sent a sample.

In an almost throwaway line I nearly didn't mention, I commented on how Dr G. Fr., didn't always have small biro handwriting, because he had written in large blue biro for the Rubella entry, and oddly enough with no initials. My mother had informed me of her Rubella concerns, and how she had gone back with my father to see Dr G. Fr.

Unpredictably Dr H. threw me a curved ball, and replied; he (Dr H.) had seen my mother for a counter measure to Rubella. On hearing this I started to argue with him this wasn't the case, and he must be getting confused, as it was a long time ago and he would have seen a lot of patients since then. Nonetheless Dr H. again restated he had been the doctor who had seen my mother for a preventative measure against Rubella. To confirm this he made an unprompted explanation that my mother was a teacher, and all the children in her class were going down with Rubella, and so she was concerned for her pregnancy.

I was confused and unsettled so tried to clarify, advising Dr H., it was unquestionably the same handwriting as all the black ink pen of Dr G. Fr. But then Dr H., informed me

A lot going on in a blue sky

this was his handwriting, and described it as large flowing and quite flamboyant. Next Dr H. confirmed he had mostly used an old fashioned black ink pen, the same as '*99%*' of the entries on the records he described. There were only about three exceptions from an earlier time of 1964 to 1965, written using biros in small handwriting with some kind of initials after them. Dr H. explained Dr G. Fr., had already retired somewhere in 1965 and therefore it could not be Dr G. Fr. in 1966, but instead the rubella entry belonged to him, Dr H.

The phone conversation had been unusual, if not for much of the time somewhat boisterously eccentric. Standing up to maintain phone signal throughout the conversation, I continued to look out the window, up at the hang-gliders and para–liders gently circling high on warm thermals.

Without warning from deep within the blue sky there was the most incredible '*single bolt of lightning*', its

An unforeseen direct strike

'100,000 volts' comprehended a direct strike, and left me literally frozen to the spot unable to move, not even the smallest fraction. The white heat of the *'lightning bolt'* conversely translated to the most chilling and shuddering shiver I have ever had run down my spine.

Instantly the full realisation and understanding hit me; the person I was and had been talking with on the other end of the phone, was the doctor who prescribed my mother Distaval/*Thalidomide*, during her pregnancy with me. This single event had defined my entire life time's existence, freeze framed at 16 weeks of foetal development from back in early March 1966; only a handful a few weeks after the Rubella visit, but five months before I was born. Now it was blatantly obvious, Dr H. was clearly the doctor my mother *"always saw"*, the *"Young one"*, not Dr G. Fr., who was an older doctor to the point of already having retired the previous year.

Abruptly it became apparent Dr H. is only four to five

years older than my parents, where as the other doctors would be around 20 to 30 years older. At the time my parents would have been in their mid to late 20's, and Dr H. would therefore have been about 30 years old. Now I could see my mother had got the doctor's names the wrong way around, but there was only ever one *'"Young one"* she *"always saw"*, and she had seen for rubella prevention, and that was Dr H.

My hunch is her misconception arose due to a single black inked stamp; Dr G. _. _. Fr., prominently placed on my mother's medical record, on the one sheet with the rubella and possible distaval entry. With no initials on any of the entries written in black flamboyant ink pen, it conveys and implies they were made by Dr. G. Fr., but all along it had been Dr H. who had written all the entries on to a prior-stamped record sheet. So it turned out my father had been right all along in thinking it was Dr H., even though my father's memory has aged and faded since 2005.

It's an appropriate point to contemplate how misinformation absorbed at medical school and during training by doctors can live with them their entire career, even long into their retirement sixty years later. Accreditation of RCOG (Royal College of Gynaecology) follows Dr H.'s name in the medical directory, and had done so from around 1963 onwards. It came across to me Dr H. considered Distaval/*Thalidomide* was widely perceived to be low if any real risk in general by the medical profession back in the 1960's. This is far less surprising on learning only a week after the supposed "withdrawal" of future sales to the wholesaler in the UK, fresh new stocks of Distaval/*Thalidomide* tablets again began to be sold to NHS Hospitals, and continued throughout 1962 [6]. Sales representatives weren't well informed during this period so the line taken was that it was OK to use with a caveat of where pregnancy could be avoided. However given wider promotional messages on *"atoxic"* and *"complete safety"*, plus continued denials of any risks during pregnancy post "withdrawal" from the wholesaler, it is doubtful such caveats were given as much emphasis as was required, and much less for use in second and third trimesters. Pressure on sales representatives would have been on the bottom line as their key focus. Who knows how many doctors were given free samples in a market awash with product? Now consider how many of these doctors working in hospitals during the early 1960's went on to become G.P.s and took the false reassurances of *Thalidomide* safety with them.

The whole tone of the conversation with Dr H. rapidly changed, and became much more defensive. He said to me, *"I don't know what I am getting myself into here, so I won't say anything more"*, and then he added, *"I've probably said too much already"*.

Before the revelation in the conversation Dr H. had agreed to comment on the entries for possible initials of *'G. F'.*, plus on another entry I had become ever more to believe was a bodged and muddied entry referring to *'dose 9 & ½ distaval MAD'*. This later entry would always be controversial, thus beyond my own interest it had no further significance, and only sought as part of personal closure.

The abbreviation of M.A.D. was something I had explored and found would fit with Hamilton's 1959/ 1960 index of assessment on Mild Anxiety and Depression or Mixed Anxiety and Depression [7]. Although another fit could be Mild Antenatal Depression? I asked Dr H., if he knew? He didn't have any ideas but said he would look at the two samples then get back to me.

Nearly two weeks later Dr H. still hadn't contacted me, so I decided to phone him. Unlike the first phone call this time Dr H. was not open, but abrupt and closed in his conversation. On the issue of the initials, Dr H. confirmed the couple of small handwritten biro entries were indeed written by Dr G. Fr., and the rest of the hand writing was his, including the counter Rubella entry, even though this was the only other entry written in biro, but without any initials.

On the entry I suspected as *'dose 9 & ½ distaval M.A.D.'*, Dr H. stated it was nothing of the sort but *'W'* (for weight), *'9 stone 5 ½ Urine N.A.D.'*. His interpretation didn't and still does not convince me, and I tried to explain some anomalies. In particular if the writing said, 'W 9 5 ½', not 'dose 9 ½', and the date '3/5/66' (3rd May 1966 as written in the UK), not a bodged 3/3/66 (3rd March 1966) that had started out as 3/2/66 as I believe, then it could not fit with that stage of pregnancy due to such little weight gain. I tried to encourage him to view the entry again and enlarge it on a computer screen, because it shows pen strokes within the letters in a new light. But he stated he knew his hand writing and it said what he had told me. The records were by then over 45 years old, they had been written in a bodged way in muddied ink and then degenerated, and beyond my own closure they had no further relevance. However whatever the entry was intended to be, Distaval/ *Thalidomide* is written down throughout me literally from head to toe, as will be evidenced in much greater detail in later chapters.

The second phone call to Dr H. was only very brief, and it was obvious there was no way he was going to admit to prescribing Distaval/ *Thalidomide*, even if it was by that point 45 years earlier. Yet Dr H. had previously advised me he commonly gave the drug to patients without any problems at a London Hospital, and in addition claimed the baby's development is completed by weeks 16, despite being an incorrect perception [4] [5, p22-p25].

From his point of view it understandable why he was very defensive, and I tried to show him empathy and remain constructive, but he advised to go any further would only be through the medical defence union. He had probably already been retired for a long time and clearly in the autumn of his years, and I had no intention of making his life more difficult at this stage.

Despite the entry concerned being bodged and all but undecipherable in many respects, for the point of view of personal closure it continued to have some interest for me. Months later I tried to contact Dr. H. again, with a request for him to write two possible interpretations of the entry concerned. It was a short and considerate correspondence explaining the main issue was not with him or any doctor per se, but instead with the drug companies that needed challenging for misleading everybody including the medical professions for over five decades. Not surprisingly he never replied, despite including a prepaid return envelope sent with tracking references that confirmed its arrival.

It is significant Distaval/*Thalidomide* in general was not often written down on patient's records, but given out like common analgesics such as aspirin, confirmed by Distillers Company Ltd; in the Sir Alan Marre Report 1978, (Section 68) Evidence of Access, p17 [8]. Distaval/*Thalidomide* was perceived as only a common analgesic and exactly the sort of drug in a doctor's kit bag, prior to the Medicines Act 1968. My mother's prescription of Distaval/ *Thalidomide* was two and half years earlier. In 1966 *Thalidomide* would still have been lurking around pharmacy shelves, plus in many G.P.'s kit bags and supporting dispensaries in various guises.

Regardless of whether Dr H. wrote down the prescription or not, I now knew he was the *"Young one"* (at the time) and prescribed Distaval/*Thalidomide* to my mother. Did Dr H. act in an extremely misguided way? Yes, but he was clearly operating in good faith on the drug companies' and government misinformation. Distillers' Company Bio-chemicals Ltd with much propaganda continued to sell Distaval/ *Thalidomide* to UK hospitals, where it was given out without adequate if any record keeping [6] [8]; during this same era Dr H. had worked in UK hospitals in the early 1960's, post "withdrawal" from the wholesale market, while the drug continued to be advertised as safe.

That summer afternoon in 2011 it's unlikely anyone else noticed the lightning strike, but it had left me feeling stunned, physically shaking, and completely out of sync. Two cups of tea in builders' style were instantly required,

Fading daylight offered unexpected clarity

but by the evening I felt the need to go for another long walk on the hills again, to mentally take it all in. Filling a water bottle I grabbed a rucksack, and within an hour I was back up at the top of the Malvern's walking along the ridge. By now the sky was less blue and had faded into notes of pink to orange to purple as part of a mellow hazy sunset, yet somehow the view for me was clearer than it had been before.

The cool evening air felt like calm after a storm, probably because for me it felt like it was. Although even today I can still feel the effects of that storm from a bolt out of a blue sky.

"Thunder is good, thunder is impressive; But it is the lightening that does the work." [9]

Mark Twain

PART IV

Shining Daylight into Some Very Dark Corners

14

Finally Coming Home Via Hollywood and Colorado

Life is a journey, as I was to consider in much greater detail in early 2013, when for a couple of days I visited a friend in Colorado. On the second floor of his house was a great view of Longs Peak, in the northern Front Range of the Rocky Mountains of North America. It was snow capped, and shrouded in hues of blue, black and orange painted in layers on to the late winter sky. For minutes at a time I would stand and absorb the timeless energy of Longs Peak. Perhaps it was the metaphor of a mountain to climb, or maybe the connection with nature, but it was here the concept of this book began to emerge.

> "The pessimist sees a difficulty in every opportunity. *The optimist sees an opportunity in every difficulty*" [1]
>
> **Winston Churchill (1874-1965)**

Only about 72 hours earlier I had no thoughts or ideas of writing a book, something brought about by an unlikely set of events. On this occasion flying out to the US from the UK had meant economically having to go via Los Angeles, despite encompassing extra unwanted travelling. Nonetheless on the plus side it offered an unanticipated opportunity to visit a specialist document analyser, to potentially decipher some handwriting on my mother's medical records. Leaving no stone unturned it seemed worth taking the chance in case it provided any new insights, not that I really expected any. On arrival none of the digital files I had taken would open on the more modern Mac computers. As neither of us were I.T. gurus, it left only a hand full of ancillary hard copies with limited detail. Andrea the document analyst was unable to confirm the entries, and advised going forward they were of little value especially considering the years of ageing. Nonetheless the materials did spark conversation, and the subject captured Andrea's interest more than I had anticipated.

Drinking some pleasant Japanese Green tea we talked further. Remarkably Andrea's work had first begun back in the mid 1960's, reviewing of all things handwritten

Green tea good company and the benefits of daylight
(Photography support: Handmade ceramics Vanessa Clark)

documents in relation to doctor's involvement in the distribution of Kevadon/ *Thalidomide*, supplied by Richardson-Merrell Inc. USA. This connection was both of real interest to me but also somewhat twilight. Her work on documents relating to Kevadon/ *Thalidomide* was probably about weeks 30 of my mother's pregnancy, only 8 to 12 weeks after I was freeze framed in foetal development at the 16 week stage by Distaval/*Thalidomide*, thousands of miles away in the UK.

For Andrea there had always been something a contradiction of how Kevadon/ *Thalidomide* was given out to patients, yet didn't ever get a licence in the US. This expanded our conversation further, and we discussed the extraordinarily resolute and diligent work by Dr Francis Kelsey that prevented the drug gaining a licence in the US. Huge financial gain was clearly the goal and focus, as Grünenthal together with Richardson–Merrell Inc. desperately tried to get a licence with the F.D.A. in the 1960's to sell Kevadon/*Thalidomide*. Whilst the US drug licence was being applied for, strategies to get around the not having a licence were already being implemented, and opened up potential for a fait–a–compleé scenario.

To these ends Richardson Merrell working with Grünenthal distributed (K17) Kevadon/ *Thalidomide* through a process of *'clinical trials'.* But in reality these were marketing trials, known as an '*Investigational Program*' [2, p98]. According to U.S. Department of Health Education and Welfare, Richardson-Merrell Inc. USA distributed 2,528,412 tablets of Kevadon/ *Thalidomide* to 1,267 doctors, who then gave the tablets to 20,000 patients [2, p98]. Plans were so far in advance of not holding a licence, distribution had already commenced at the end of the 1950's, 18 months prior to their application [3, p42]. Most likely inevitably some people in the US were subjected to Kevadon/ *Thalidomide* and negatively affected, but did not receive enough if any recognition. Reports have suggested out of stocks totalling about 5 tonnes, 2 tonnes, i.e. over a million tablets of Kevadon/ *Thalidomide (k17)* remained unaccounted for [4].

About 6 months after my mother took Distaval/ *Thalidomide* in the UK, action in the US tightened such loopholes; ending the distribution of new drugs through so called *'Clinical/ marketing trials'/ 'Investigational Programs'*, prior to obtaining full certification and licences [5, p346-p349]. Although it is quite possible Kevadon/ *Thalidomide* may have been prescribed at some level for some situations in the US, like it was during March 1966 in my case. Not least due to its global marketed status of a universal panacea that was *"completely safe"*, and *"atoxic"*. It is likely in practical terms, any updated regulation in the autumn of 1966 may have taken a bit longer to be fully implemented on the ground. The full potential extent for disaster in the USA was beyond comprehension, and is covered more in Chapter 20, *A Heroine, and Betsy Andreu's Courage.*

> ## "If your cold tea will warm you, If your hot tea will cool you, If your depressed tea will cheer you, If your excited tea will calm you" [6]
>
> ### Gladstone

Returning to the moment in early 2013 and late morning Los Angeles winter sunshine poured through the window.

Now onto my second cup of Japanese Green tea I was enjoying the conversation, and we talked further on what it all meant in human terms. A theme developed by pointing out some of my visible biomarkers; ear positions, hand size, cubit and foot size. Next I explained how I had seen bio–markers on x-rays of my skull revealing my bone structure is of a 16 week foetal skull, not the completed development of a full term neonatal skull. Using a diagrammatic representation of foetal skulls at 12, 16 Weeks and Full Term Weeks from a sample of 'Life-ART' illustration by L.W.W. 1989-2001© [7] I pointed out some salient relevant developmental features.

At first I had thought Andrea's attentiveness to the issue was because of links to her work back in the 1960's, however by now I had sensed her concern was also from the perspective of a woman, and as a mother. Andrea asked me, *"What do you want to achieve?"* My reply was instinctive; *"Update the text books on the misinformation on* Distaval/ *Thalidomide, and all that has remained unacknowledged so far".* Out of the blue, Andrea made a comeback that was more of a question than a statement; *"You could write a book...why don't you write your own book"?*

This was not unlike how my mother may have put it to me, and perhaps what made it so powerful. In that moment I froze as my mind instantly flashed back seven years earlier to my mother's final days, and how she had let me know she wanted me to take these issues forward. Up to then I had always thought of going through official channels. However by then I had also become aware it was the official channels that were the problem, not the solution, but producing a book could finally provide her with a voice.

Despite that Andrea was only offering an empathetic suggestion, I also felt stunned. Part of me didn't think it was possible, or I was able to do it. For a start how would I manage to hold everything else in life together, and get by? Things had been on a real slide outside my control ever since the economic crisis took hold in 2008, and by early 2013 new options seemed nonexistent. It had left life boxed in on all sides, but regardless I said I would write a book, although I wasn't sure what the book would be, or if it was really possible.

Over the time of writing this book life continued to slide, as various additional challenges came in sideways. Every spare hour was given to typing up research and drafts of chapters. This was so much that at times the walls would feel like they were starting to come in. Yet conversely it was also a metaphor and a process of breaking free from silently being boxed in, for a life time to the 16 week stage of foetal development.

Following our meeting Andrea gave me a handful of sealed Japanese Green tea bags, then a lift back to the centre of Los Angeles. Over the next day while flying on to Colorado, I reflected in depth on whether it was going to be practical or realistic to write a book. Nonetheless I could see the empowering potential, plus how a book would finally provide a voice for all the people silenced on the issues concerned. At its most simple, it required bringing it all back to the human level, very much as in the conversation over cups of Japanese Green Tea.

"You can only write about what bites you" [8]

Tom Stoppard

Before such time there were no more intentions of making a film, than there were of writing a book, and there are still no intentions of making a movie, not even to get one of those star things put in the pavement.

All the same, was it destiny unwittingly being in Hollywood the same time as the acting fraternity and famous turned up for the 2013 OSCARS®? There were no invites for me to attend along with the stars of the big silver screen, not even at the start of the introductory walk on the red carpet up to the big Dolby Theatre. None of that mattered though, because for me a greater and more significant prize had just been won.

Out of a decade of fog and searching I began to comprehend how all the events on the Distaval/ *Thalidomide* trail had been a journey. A deep and complex one, if not at times both challenging in terms of self–discovery and of wider unsettling societal issues, however now I had a way to express and communicate all the insights gained over many years.

The final evening before returning to the UK, was spent with my Colorado friend Ross and family. We talked over how these events had been an epic personal journey. On the theme of challenging the status quo in connection to environmental concerns, Ross asked me, *"Do you know about Erin Brockovich? – they made a movie about it all"… starred Julia Roberts"*. A year to the day whilst provisionally working on this chapter I watched the movie broadcast on TV back in the UK. He asked how far I was through resolving the Distaval/*Thalidomide* issues if it were a ten chapter book. Intuitively and without delay I replied, *"Chapter 8, maybe chapter 9"*, but acknowledged only *"72 hours earlier, it felt more like chapter 3 or 4"*. He said writing a book would take *"three years"*, although his wife

Peggy kindly suggested it might only take *"two"*. With life's ups and downs it took about 5.

On the drive to the airport the next day there was a great view of Longs Peak through the Aspen trees, and the clean sparkling Colorado winter air. In that moment I realised how the trip to the US had been a great success, although not in ways remotely conceived of or anticipated before leaving the UK only 10 days earlier. Now I had the most important job of my life to do. This was to communicate as much as possible of the unaccounted history and misinformation of Distaval/ *Thalidomide*, expressed at the human level.

Rolls Royce precision engineered turbines purred flawlessly at hundreds of thousands of R.P.M. all the way back across the Atlantic, and safely brought the aeroplane home to the UK. It's often said it is darkest before the dawn, but somehow arriving at daybreak through a midlands greyish nondescript sky the sun was most definitely up. The planes wheels lightly bounced contact on the runway, and the turbo fans were switched down low to a numbing hush. Unbelievable as it was ironic, it was also exactly 47 years to the week, and probably even the very day, since my personal journey and the narrative of this book originally began. Perhaps this helped consolidate the title of *"16 Weeks and Everything After..."*©; but either way I now knew it was game on again, because at last I was finally coming home via Hollywood, and Colorado.

"They say time changes things, but you actually have to change them yourself" [9]

Andy Warhol

15

Nature Never Hides or Misrepresents Anything

Over the last 15 years I have learnt a lot relating to *Thalidomide*, and often from unexpected angles. One set of insights would shed light into other things laterally, then combine and create joined up thinking elsewhere. An especially pertinent understanding has been how ultimately nature always reveals what's occurred in an environment. For example a tree on an exposed hill top or cliff edge, where the wind has blown predominantly in one direction over years, the tree always leans compliantly the same direction the wind has blown. Inside its cell structure will divulge growth rings and grain forms in a non-rounded way that produces a narrowing effect [1].

If we pay attention nature often reveals even greater insights inside

When a tree is cut through it reveals its history and the environment it was in, even where no apparent external signs of biomarkers are evident, inside will provide all hidden accounts. Tree rings indicate age plus environmental conditions the tree lived through; for example, available water levels, or not, with drier years producing thinner tree rings. Over a trees lifetime it keeps a diary/ journal of the climate measuring any changes [1], along with other environmental stressors also.

Nature is shouting out to humankind the mistakes we are making in the environment. Many suggest bees are telling us much more than we have so far been listening to. Adverse effects in bee populations is highly likely related to environmental factors, and some have suggested Wi-Fi and mobile signal a factor [2]. Pesticides and agrochemicals such as neonicatoides have also been shown to be detrimental to bee populations [3].

Paul Whymark Photography ©

Often bio-indication gives answers before we have worked out the right questions

"Patience and tenacity are worth more than twice their weight in cleverness" [(4)]

Thomas Huxley, English Biologist 1825–1895

Ultimately nature has a way of informing us of what is really going on in an environment, revealing the real consequences through bioindication. These provide more accurate information where other scientific approaches fail to observe, detect or report with transparency, because nature runs 24/7 real time recording of biomarkers for all environmental consequences.

In 2008 and 2009 during pond dipping exercises at F.S.C. Preston Montford I began to see how biomarker evidence from Distaval/*Thalidomide* exposure during pregnancy would be revealed as 24/7 exposure records in the form of biomarkers. Applied laterally, it reveals embryogenesis impacts during pregnancy shown as gestational biomarkers from 24/7 real time recording. In my case this was and is for foetal development between weeks 16 to 20 of gestation. Although on learning of this concept I remained unaware my skull is, and always has been a biomarker of a 16 week foetal skull. Now of course it is so unbelievably obvious my skull is a 16 week foetal development biomarker, like everything else within me. It took me three to four years after my mother's life was over before I comprehended this, and over four further years to get the x-ray shown below. Nonetheless the results are unambiguous and conclusive; Distaval/ *Thalidomide* does, and always has had the potential to negatively impact on a developing foetus between weeks 16 to 20, leaving specific timeline biomarkers for a lifetime to confirm it.

In the early 1960's Dr Francis Kelsey, working for the

F.D.A. had sensed polyneuritis effects of *Thalidomide* provided real warning signs of the potential to harm developing babies at any stage of pregnancy [5, p112-p130]. Not least because another of her insights from previous pharmacological work revealed how the developing foetus was functioning as a quite different organism compared to an adult.

Dr Francis Kelsey was right, graphically shown in my skull and vertebrae x-ray. There are 10 biomarker examples instantly evident revealing my development as a foetus was freeze-framed at the 16 weeks stage of foetal development while exposed to Distaval/ *Thalidomide*.

On one occasion I showed a doctor the x-ray in this chapter. Their instant reaction was, *"What happened there"?* The x-ray is of my skull and the result of being exposed to one of the world's worst teratogenic drugs ever, *Thalidomide*. These biomarker finding provides real life eco-validity exactly as would be predicted by *Thalidomide* antiangiogenesis action, on developing cells definatively evidenced in studies by Dr Neil Vargesson at Aberdeen.

The 16 week time scale of *Thalidomide* exposure reveals without doubt harm occurs at least over double the time period previously acknowledged of the first 9 weeks; worse still only selected days within the so called '9 week sensitive period' were officially recognised. The *Thalidomide* establishment did not want you to see my skull x-ray, and less appreciate what it means for the false claims they made for 50 years. Nonetheless it is clear that it is now time to update the text books.

Biomarkers in my skull provide much greater significance than harms only to my skull, although clearly that is very significant. As my 16 week foetal skull bone structures at the time were the most advanced, this also

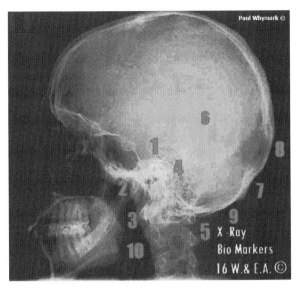

Impacts of **Distaval**/ Thalidomide at 16 weeks of foetal
development last a life time

demonstrates *Thalidomide* harms went far further than
what is shown in my x-ray. These bone structures in foetal
skulls are amongst the very first bones to start to move
from cartilage to bone composition. Consequently these
bone structures would have been the most resistant to
harms inflicted by *Thalidomide*. Thus it can be concluded
with absolute certainty all other cells also trying to develop
in the same time frame were impaired to a much greater
extent; especially all developing brain cells and neurons
only millimetres away from my skull. Brain cells are even
more susceptible to being damaged from the negative
impacts of *Thalidomide* harm that would have occurred on
all other cells trying to develop in me at 16 to 20 weeks of
gestation [6, p54-p65] [7, p22-p25].

Hence my bilateral skeletal system presents reduced
leg and arm length, and especially proportions in my lower

limbs. My hands and feet are yet further biomarkers right down to an absence of cuticles on my finger nails [6, p172-p173] [8, p178]. All would otherwise have continued to develop and enlarge during weeks 16 to 20 of embryogenesis, to reach my genetic final destined proportions and form.

Two to three years before my mother was given *Thalidomide*, experiments on rats in the early 1960's by King and Kendrick revealed the drug caused more subtle internal damage, including skeletal/ spine structures. Initially these rats appeared externally to have no anomalies or malformations. However x-rays and post-mortems revealed overlooked damage had occurred internally [9], including a subcutaneous cartilaginous type mass of tissue from the mid-dorsal region to the tail.

At only a glance compared to a regular adult male skull, the *Thalidomide* damage and impairments of development in me are obvious [10] [11, p28-p29, p43]. This is why my ears are at the position of a 16 week foetus, because the skull architecture had not, and did not fully form beyond this stage. Hence consequently my ears could not move beyond the point they were at 16 weeks. Thus they remain in the same position over 50 years on, and always will be [10] [6, p23 B+C].

The more deeply profound insight however is the indirect confirmation that my brain formation was without doubt impeded. To state the obvious it can be summed up in the phrase; *"A quart can't fit into a pint pot"* (N.B quart = 2 pints). Clearly as my skull size and form did not reach its full size and proportions then my brain did not have the required space to develop either [6, p54-p65] [7, p22-p25].

Biomarker # 7 is highly significant as it shows a deep intrusion in the middle of the occipital bone. N.B. Regular completed skulls have an extrusion at this point [11, p28-p29, p98, p100-p103), facilitating more internal space for the brain to form and develop into. The tip of the brains occipital lobe would otherwise reside in this space and may have more than one function or role, but it is associated with differentiating fine detail used in reading (12, p386-p389). Thus this lack of this area/ space in my skull accounts for the missing brain development, and has resulted in Irlen Syndrome/ Scotopic Sensitivity; hence my inability to read a mass of text/ abstract symbols close together on a page, without them all confusingly swimming around. Plus why viewing the world through a hue of orange lenses enables my general vision to see detail, for example branches in trees.

Biomarkers # 8 and 9 are the occipital bone lying low on the back of the skull; over stretched it has pushed Biomarker # 4 the mastoid bone (11, p28-p29, p43) into a arrangement being turned up more like 90° vertically rather than the reclined horizontal position it would have achieved if my skull had been allowed to fully develop. Biomarkers # 5 and # 10 show a spine leaning the wrong way, and without a step or offset at the end of the spinal column, plus perhaps some bone fusions? Either way my spine and skull remain in the format of a 16 week foetus.

Biomarkers # 1, # 2 and # 3 provide definitive indisputable evidence foetal development in me did not go beyond the 16 week stage of gestation, as my skull development did not progress beyond the 16 week foetal precursory bone structures known as the tympanic ring (10) (8, p12-14, p90-p92, p197-p198) (13, p32) (14, p326). In regular development not impaired or negatively impacted by *Thalidomide*, the tympanic ring morphs shape and decreases in size to become the opening into the acoustic meatus; a small tube type opening for the neural-audible pathway for hearing.

Clearly I was extremely lucky not to have had a lifetime of significantly reduced and impaired hearing. The outcome if Distaval/ *Thalidomide* had been taken only one day earlier for me may have notably reduced my hearing and therefore life experience more universally.

Biomarker # 6 is the parietal bone presentation in me remaining as it would be at weeks 16 of foetal development [10] [11 p28-p29, p43]. The skull would have the location of brain areas around the temporal lobe that includes parts of the brain for the phonological loop, including Broca's and Wernickers; used for language and learning [12, p386-p390]. The susceptibility of brain cells to be damaged and or impeded in development is again hugely significant [7, p22-p25]. This provides yet more damning substantiation Distaval/ *Thalidomide* harmed and impaired the key areas of my brain for reading and processing of information.

Evidently *Thalidomide* halted my bone/ cartilage development, and therefore it is 100% certain the drug stopped neurons and synaptic connections forming, as these structures are considerably more susceptible to harm. Given mental retardation increases significantly where damage occurs as late as weeks 15, this is profound [15, p420]. It indicates that had the Distaval/ *Thalidomide* Tablets perhaps been taken even only 24 hours earlier then this book may not have been possible; and the drug companies' et al would have got away with their unchallenged legacy of misinformation.

On first making self discoveries using the *'Paulo-Dual Mapping Process'* (see Chapter 6 Mapping Connections by Connection Mapping), I did not know my skull had not formed in the relevant areas. In addition the same implications apply to all other areas of my brain that would have otherwise developed at and during weeks 16 to 20 of foetal development [7, p22-p25].

Less obvious biomarkers are present in my skull sutures, and these too show a freeze frame of a 16 week skull, (to some extent less obvious in the x-ray) yet these also reveal both unilateral and bilateral presentations. The squamous suture and the sphenoidal fontanelle are aligned with the frontal bone and parietal bone is also off set in angle and form, plus these are higher in me, at around the top of occipital socket not the lower part [10] [11, p28-p29, p43]. This is more visible in real life than on the x-ray, but does present slightly around the area above biomarker #1 and back to # 6, if looking at the gradient of colour density. The lambdoid suture where the parietal bone joins the occipital bone, below #6 and above #7, #8 and #9 is set way high as those bones did not fully form beyond 16 weeks [11, p28-p29, p43]. On the top of my skull the coronal suture leads down one side as expected and the other the bone structure has not quite differentiated enough, consequently pulling a slight morphed malformed suture [11, p28-p29, p43]. This is the only anomalous unilateral *Thalidomide* malformation of embryogenesis in me, I have discovered. All other areas presenting as equal bilateral harms, suggesting this small asymmetry in my foetal growth occurred from a dose of *Thalidomide* probably only hours or even minutes before it would have developed.

These biomarkers reveal *Thalidomide* harms developing human life at and on every stage of pregnancy through its aggressive action of antiangiogenesis [16]. It confirms the limitations of a 9 week sensitive period are bogus, flawed, errant and a myth. This means every day in all of the firsts 9 weeks plus all remaining 31 weeks of the entire pregnancy are potentially sensitive to the harmful effects of *Thalidomide* (or analogues of). *Thalidomide* has the power to potentially damage every cell, every system, every sense plus every organ in the body, and also cause multiple affects of harm.

It is really important to appreciate what this means in reality. The spectrum of harms inflicted by *Thalidomide* will have been far boarder and more extensive than is officially on record. Its insidious affects are capable of damaging all sensory functions; sight, hearing, touch, taste, smell, and in addition potential for harm to all organs including and especially the brain, plus all systems that make up a human body. Due to the unrecognised status of many such impairment or health complications, it is most likely not even the person harmed by *Thalidomide,* or their family, will have been aware the drug was the cause.

Ironic then as it is incongruous, but it has taken the cerebral insights of a 16 week foetal brain; to outwit and outsmart 50 to 60 years of the entire combined intellectual acumen of the establishment and corporate world. But then sometimes in life, it's funny how things work out. Vested conflicts of interests have failed to communicate for decades the full potential of *Thalidomide* harms in an open, objective and transparent way. However nature has the power to inform, illuminate and shine daylight into such dark corners, because ultimately, nature never hides or misrepresents anything.

Silent Spring, By Rachel Carlson [17]
First Published in 1962/ 1965,
50th Anniversary Edition 2015

"Silent Spring is a devastating attack on human carelessness, greed and irresponsibility. It should be read by every American who does not want to be the epitaph of a world not very far beyond us in time"

'Saturday Review'

16

A Corporate Garden Path

Before *Thalidomide* even came to market in the 1950's, extremely unsettling data had already been obtained revealing it was not a safe drug, but instead was very harmful, and even a potentially fatal drug [1, p136-p137] [2, p96-p98]. Evidence in the 1950's even showed *Thalidomide* caused serious malformations during human pregnancy [2, p96-p98], but somehow this too got overlooked. Tests for Grünenthal at Smith Kline & French ended further joint involvement with a conclusion *Thalidomide*'s apparent harmlessness was because it was believed the drug was not being effectively absorbed [1, p136]. Yet none of the

In a field of freezing fog hearing becomes muted and vision is obscured

above prevented Grünenthal and other *Thalidomide* drug companies marketing it as *"Atoxic"* and *"Completely Safe"*, and then selling huge quantities worldwide.

The history of *Thalidomide* presentations could be described as fogging and freezing out transparency. Richardson-Merrell around 1960 worked with Grünenthal to bring *Thalidomide* to the US market, made some tests on Rats with highly disturbing results. Using a syrup solution *Thalidomide* was given to 11 rats: 5 male and 6 female. All six females in the experiment died. More damning scientific evidence followed in further research, where *Thalidomide* was given to 30 male rats as in the previous study. Here 22 died the same day, plus another the next day, i.e. 23 out of 30, a lethal attrition rate of c.77% [2, p96-p98]. These studies alone should have been enough for *Thalidomide* to have been completely stopped for use in all stages of pregnancy.

Despite demonstrating *Thalidomide* was a very unsafe and hazardous drug, further studies showed even more alarming evidence. In follow up work, 37 rats were subjected to *Thalidomide*; 32 were killed outright on the same day, plus all of the remaining 5 rats died the following day [2, p96-p98]; that is a 100% lethal attrition rate caused by a drug claimed to be *"completely safe"* and *"atoxic"*. At Richardson-Merrell a dog was subjected *Thalidomide* in case there was some strange over sensitivity in rats. The dog was put under serious strain; it trembled through its entire body, twitched, retched and vomited. For two hours forty five minutes after the dog appeared normal, but then became hyper active and staggered around its cage unable to control or co-ordinate its muscles. By the next morning the dog was dead [2 p96-p98], another *Thalidomide* experiment with 100% fatal attrition.

On application for a licence for *Thalidomide* in the US

none of this information was passed onto Dr Kelsey at the F.D.A, or any officials elsewhere in the world. In the years since *Thalidomide* "withdrawal" from the wholesaler a great deal more science has been obscured, miss presented, misdirected or misguidedly focused. Grünenthal and other *Thalidomide* drug companies/ settlement bodies have carefully spun an errant narrative from the 1960's onward. As a result the wool has been pulled over the eyes of entire professions and the public alike.

In the UK Distillers Company Bio-chemicals Ltd initially sought to keep *Thalidomide* available for something, even if they hadn't worked out exactly for what. Behind the scenes contacts with the editor of Lancet tried to get doctors to write in for Distaval (*Thalidomide*) to be put back on the market. Initially the drug went into hospitals after the official "withdrawal for the wholesaler". As this avenue didn't make economic headway by December 1962, a year later further sales of Distaval to hospitals were finally halted [2, p146].

However not everybody had believed the spin and presentation on *Thalidomide* safety. More enquiring minds had concerns, as some medics began suspecting a probable link to *Thalidomide* use for morning sickness and the unprecedented increase in server and serious malformations in new babies at birth. In the first instance it was Dr McBride in Australia [2, p14-p20] and Dr Lenz in Germany who first sensed *Thalidomide* was the culprit behind the rise in serious malformations [3, p94-p104]. The magnitude was very sobering, and for understandable reasons focused urgent and immediate efforts to determine if the more server harms of phocomelia were arising from *Thalidomide*. However this focus created a vacuum and meant lesser and other harms the drug caused were not adequately considered and therefore much less investigated.

From 1962 new lines of enquiry began. Dr Somers head of pharmacology at Distillers Company Bio-chemicals Ltd found rabbit malformations replicated types of damage seen in humans [4]. He swiftly reported his findings to the lancet despite being requested not to by the drug companies [2, p145]. *Thalidomide* had already arrived at Distillers Bio-chemicals Ltd before Dr Somers became appointed as head pharmacologist. He later said if he had been there at the beginning to test the compound he, *"would have thrown it out the window"* [5, p16].

Studies on chicks showed wing and leg malformations' much as for limbs in humans [6]. Other damage included beak, skull and eyes [7], indicating *Thalidomide* harms were not limited to only arm and leg damage. Human development is on a considerably more sophisticated level, especially concerning head and brain development. Hence this provided highly pertinent warnings and indicators of likely harmful effects on humans in later pregnancy. Further studies in primates [8] [9] [10] showed similar limb and other damage as in humans. How much those studies looked beyond an assumed but bogus *"sensitive period"* is doubtful, but evidence may have extended to the end of the first trimester if enough attention was paid? When Distillers Company Bio-chemicals Ltd put *Thalidomide* (in various brands) onto the market they had made no prior testing on animals during in pregnancy. In addition no testing concerning *Thalidomide* use in later pregnancy appears to have been made since with objective and open criteria.

Distillers Company Ltd operated naively and took at face value claims the drug was "completely safe" and "atoxic". Hence in 1958 when Grünenthal in a letter to German physicians declared *Thalidomide* was the best drug for pregnant women, Distillers Co. Ltd also added this to their list of claims for the drug [5, p17]. On the arrival of Dr Somers, he became increasingly concerned about the safety of *Thalidomide* and was sceptical of toxicity tests, especially on discovering side effects in rodents. Dr Somers even made a visit to Germany to Grünenthal concerning some doubtful rat tests, but was fobbed off with the spin it was just a batch of over sensitive rodents producing some unreliable results [3, p182-p184]. Dr Somers had no evidence to the contrary to counter Grünenthal, and initially had to live with the apparent scientific anomalies; until he and others managed to produce harder evidence to substantiate his concerns. Grüthenthal and Distillers Company Ltd Directors continued to keep *Thalidomide* safety issues an intra and in house affair [2, p82-p89].

Early tests on rats and mice didn't fully consider dose proportions compared to humans, or how absorption rates varied depending on the medium used to give the drug [2, p72]. Sugar and syrup solutions sped up absorption rates and showed increased risks of toxicity [2, p82-p86]. However not all female rats produced malformed offspring, as embryos were being reabsorbed. This meant no malformed offspring were recorded [11], but it was not healthy for the mother rat as potential complications could develop. Relative high doses tended to lead to reabsorbing of the foetus in rats, although that was not appreciated early on; more examples of not asking the right questions.

To bring *Thalidomide* to market Grünenthal conducted some very strange scientific enquiry, probably better described as pseudo science that was not replicable by others in future years. One of the most bizarre tests in the 1950's was the so called *"Jiggle Cage"*. It was more like fantasy than science and claimed to be used to determine if a rat was asleep, for the purposes of marketing *Thalidomide* as a sedative [2, p27-p39]. Out of these experiments claims were made it demonstrated rats became drugged with *Thalidomide* to a point where they were not conscious enough to stand up, and thus it was claimed showed sedation [1, p58-p60]. Latter these results became highly disputed. Dr Lenz stated *"The author claims to have shown a sleep inducing effect, though no sleep was observed"*. Dr Lenz highlighted other pharmaceutical companies were unable to replicate these claims [1, p58-p60], and wondered what Grünenthal had done?

The rising numbers of major malformations in human babies, and the extent of information withheld by the drug companies, resulted in fraught and desperate attempts to try and find immediate answers. Data provided an almost perfect correlation with the rising numbers, and the prior increased use of *Thalidomide* taken by women for morning sickness in the first 9 week of pregnancy [3, p156].

Number crunching pointed to correlations for a match to the bias selected i.e. serve phocomelia (absence of arm or leg development). Bias tends to reflect what has been selected as criteria, sometimes referred to as selection bias, because it does not reflect or indicate what has not been considered. The statistics showing an almost perfect association with babies with serve phocomelia and use of *Thalidomide* in the first 9 weeks was undoubtedly right. Yet it was not measuring all of the other affects of *Thalidomide* during different embryogenesis time windows. Hence therefore statistics did not seek to measure other issues, other time frames or combinations of both.

There were two intrinsic inbuilt filters used in the

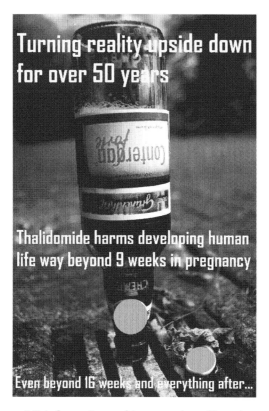

Misinformation and inaccuracies still need
correcting in text books old and new

statistics, and these masked all concurrent variables within
collected data i.e. there was more than one thing going on
at the same time but only one consideration was sought
to be measured. The majority of women who get morning
sickness tend to suffer during the first 9 weeks, despite
not being the case for all women. However thus it became
a self fulfilling prophecy, as conclusions only concerned
issues of the first 9 weeks time frame, but the statistics
did nothing to consider levels and degrees of harm in later
time frames. Therefore the statistics could not, and hence

did not reflect the risks and lack of safety in later week's, 10 11, 12, 13, 14, 15, 16, 17, 18, 19, 20, or any week through to neonatal weeks 40.

A situation arose where the limits of *Thalidomide* induced harms were based on retrospective guesswork. The first assumption were *Thalidomide* only caused babies to be born with phocomelia i.e. arms or legs very significantly reduced in size or even none at all. Yet this did not consider babies who died before birth or just after, even though later it was realised many babies didn't survive beyond birth.

Degrees and extent of injuries and malformations went far further than the guessed at criteria, and were no doubt systemic for both babies who survived and for those who did not. Retrospective analysis can have real issues, particularly where inaccurate criteria are selected or assumed, regardless of however well intentioned. Consequently inaccuracies become compounded and lead to further errors of judgment going forward, because they underpinned the next erroneous level of protocol criteria. This occurred with assessment of the numbers of *Thalidomide* injuries and malformations.

To start with doctors had no idea what malformations or medical complications they were even looking for. Which ones should be left in or out, if any or even why? The only knowledge to act on was the birth of a malformed baby without complete arms or legs, and the awareness (in some cases, but not all) the drug *Thalidomide* having been taken by an expectant mother in the first 9 week period of pregnancy. A protocol emerged where babies presented with significant phocomelia (seal like arms and legs), and this became attributed to *Thalidomide*.

Although it is important to appreciate the drug

companies denied any proof existed for even the most server *Thalidomide* harms for years. Another limiting, irrational and flawed assumption was *Thalidomide* harms could only occur as bilateral damage i.e. a flawed interpretation claiming equal damage had to be replicated in right and left arms, or both legs, or all limbs. These guessed assumptions were grossly inaccurate as *Thalidomide* can easily cause unilateral harms, as on occasions the embryo and foetus may, in terms of time, develop very slightly asymmetrically. Even if only very slightly, but enough for given time frames to co-inside with a single dose of *Thalidomide*, thus the other side an embryo or foetus remained unexposed and therefore develops as expected. Yet it took about a further 15 years, around 1978 before this began to achieve some wider acknowledgement in medical thinking [12], but even then most of the public probably remained unaware.

The central point to take from the above is how any methodology of retrospective observational analysis undertaken in this way is very prone to being inaccurate. Such processes only measures what the observer/ clinician/ researcher puts in to an assessing process (by accident, or by choice). The equally if not more pertinent point, is how by implication this aspect excludes objective consideration of all it leaves out. In the case of *Thalidomide* harms, a great deal was left out between weeks 9 and 40 of pregnancy, not to mention some of what occurred within and up to 9 weeks.

Over two months before I was born, but almost two months after I was freeze framed at the stage of 16 week foetal development, research appeared in the Lancet reporting ocular (sight) damage to babies had been associated with *Thalidomide* [13]. It noted 25% of babies deemed to be *Thalidomide* survivors had eye complications. At one level this was research progress, but it only considered a selected cohort within a predetermined phase of embryogenesis. No doubt all those people were harmed by *Thalidomide*, but it could not, and did not say what other harms to eyesight may occur beyond the 9 week time frame.

A steer on the direction of investigation and future research had been formed by limiting findings to only a selected sub set of major malformations, associated with the first 8 to 9 weeks of pregnancy (which is the embryonic phase, not the foetal phase post 9 weeks). This became the official line and laid the foundation for the neural crest theory/ hypothesis, as around weeks 9 the neural crest has formed which is the rudimentary foundation of the brain hence the theory and its name [14, p8]. In addition elementary toes and fingers have also formed.

The claim was *Thalidomide* attacked nerve formation only in the first 9 weeks; hence said to prevent limbs development only in their earliest stages of formation. This picked up on noted polyneuritis side effects in adults caused by *Thalidomide*, but missed the real point that nerve harm in adults was a resulting side effect, not the causation. The neural crest theory/ hypothesis derived from x-ray analysis, and projected different types of *Thalidomide* presentation would unfold as pregnancy went on, in a partly explicable but partly mysterious way. Tied to this flawed perspective, interpretations made even more restricting claims *Thalidomide* harms could only happen on specific days within the 9 weeks, to specific parts of the body. For example the theory emerged harm to ear development only occurred on certain days; [1, p195-p207] while limits on legs and arms development malformations also got wrongly assigned to only a few specified days around when limbs were budding.

Dr. McCredie became the main proponent as the neural crest theory/ hypothesis grew in prominence during the 1970's. It is likely work by Dr McCredie over years will have made some indirect insights into aspects of pre birth development. It is the case some of the more extreme harms from *Thalidomide* do occur during the first 9 week timescales. Her sincerity and dedication in pursuit of understanding *Thalidomide* harm are not at issue.

However regrettably the neural crest theory/ hypothesis let cynical powerful forces of the *Thalidomide* drug companies/ settlement bodies/trusts off the hook, while gaining a narrative for their propaganda. It allowed a theme to develop claiming some strange mysterious but undecipherable attack on nerves and nerve endings occurred on only very specific days within the first 9 weeks, and these would be the only times when the drug could harm the unborn.

Yet there has always been an obvious contradiction to such narratives. If *Thalidomide* primarily attacked nerves and nerve endings, it would mean the drug would always above all else would attack where ever there would be a high level of nerves, e.g. spines and brains including controls for breathing, heart rate and life support systems etc, long before attacking other anatomical structures. But this clearly did not happen, and instead an almost infinite range of malformations, damage, harm and impairment across the whole spectrum of development and extent of development occurred but was never accounted for or recognised.

The neural crest theory/ hypothesis of development harm from *Thalidomide* exposure does not remotely begin to account for all the potential full range of damage possible. For example it doesn't allow the prospect of my skull x-ray revealing I was freeze framed at 16 weeks of foetal development.

Dr Neil Vargesson's work demonstrated the harmful action of *Thalidomide* on developing babies is antiangiogenesis [15]. This does explain how harm is caused at the limb budding stages, but also antiangiogenesis doesn't have a limited time period to harm the unborn. Hence *Thalidomide* can and does damage the embryo at 16 days, and also impair and harm foetal development at 112 days (16 weeks). All the aspects are freeze framed in me at weeks 16 of foetal development including limb proportions, ear position etc.

The neural crest theory/ hypothesis provided excuses of multiple limitations of harm from *Thalidomide* exposure, and denial of far more wide ranging injuries. No surprise this was like music to the ears of the drug companies and liability holders; as it enabled all debate of other well reasoned lines of enquiry in all further medical and public discussion to be shut down and blocked.

There were a handful of individuals brave enough to challenge the power of *Thalidomide* drug companies and the naive leadership within medical institutions. Dr Poswillo in the 1970's made long term clinical studies [17, p67-p73] [18], and realised the neural crest theory/ hypothesis and the 9 week sensitive period did not explain or account for the myriad of *Thalidomide* harms he saw over years of clinical observations. Dr Poswillo could physically see in clinical studies links to work by Jurrand from the 1960's evidencing haemorrhaging malformations in animal tests [18]. Hence he believed the answers to *Thalidomide* harms lay in effects on the blood system, not as a result of malformed nerve development.

"To some extent, we are all labelled by what we're able to achieve; But more importantly, we are defined by what we attempt" [16]

Scott Tinley
(1980's Pioneering World Class Tri-athlete)

Over four decades later, it has been shown by Jurrand et al., they were on the right lines along. The action of antiangiogenesis occurs by the shutting down of blood supply and preventing the formation of the vascular system, and hence everything else that develops using a vascular system; which is clearly everything. It points to why some previous studies had evidence of animals presented with breathing difficulties, when given high doses of *Thalidomide*, i.e. the vascular system is shut down so therefore oxygen supply is reduced, plus waste build up may create issues. Ironic but Jurrand's paper noting harm to the blood system and haemorrhaging injuries [19] was published around my 19th week of foetal development around 23rd March 1966 while I was still being exposed to Distaval/*Thalidomide*.

In the late 1970's a number of other particularly distinguished professionals including developmental biologist Professor Lewis Wolpert questioned the legitimacy of the neural crest, suggesting its validity was not only week but also contrary to other known embryological studies [1, p200]. Dr Claus Newman was another prominent doctor with real concerns on how the methodology used for making assumptions of limited injuries in limited earlier stages of pregnancy could not account for other injuries at later times [1, p198-p199]. Dr Poswillo, Dr Newman, Jurrand and other more enlightened people were ignored by the establishment right up to and including the Sir Allan Marre report in 1978 [17, p67-p73].

The 1978 Sir Allan Marre report was the last time there was even so much as a half attempt to publically review limitations of *Thalidomide* harms, but it left only a fudged whitewash with contradictions. Some unilateral injuries and malformations became semi-acknowledged and the myth of only a limited 9 week sensitive period was in part modified to accommodate some more cases in weeks 10 to 12. Yet as the neural crest formation has taken place with the embryo becoming a foetus at c.9 weeks [14, p2-p9], these illogical adjustments only demonstrated further cognitive dissonance.

To accommodate the neural crest theory/ hypothesis as the only option, other than to admit it had always been wrong and there would be much wider issues meant 16 year later; extending timeframes to integrate a handful of new accepted *Thalidomide* harms meant also claiming extending the mysterious properties of the drug. Regardless of irrational changes to the retained erroneous doctrine, time frames were not extended nearly enough to cover all the harms that occurred.

As a result *Thalidomide* drug companies and government responsibilities for further testing and transparency once again got sidestepped, leaving in place the legacy of erroneous interpretations to be perpetually propagated. Medical objectivity concerning the risks and harms caused by *Thalidomide* during pregnancy had again been subjugated at an institutional and inter-institutional level that has remained to the present day. Consequently the text books since have kept repeating the same bogus errant misinformation which only serves to mislead future generations of medics around the world.

Today I realise this is what the consultant was referring to concerning unilateral and bilateral biometrics within me in childhood. The consultant on child growth and development who I visited in the 1970's would have been aware of clinical accounts by Dr Poswillo, and science by Jurrand [2, p343] [19] (published while I was being exposed to *Thalidomide* in March 1966) but the consultant would have been powerless against the might of *Thalidomide* drug companies' airbrushed account. My hunch is he would have met and seen many people throughout childhood over years he most likely believed had been negatively impacted by *Thalidomide*, yet at the same time could not express this in his professional capacity.

Incongruously in an unpublished 1978 manuscript, the then medical officer for TTUK, Dr (Earnest) Philip Quibell, concluded a huge number of people affected by *Thalidomide* had not been recognised due to erroneous assessments [1, p200]. Dr Quibell was a renowned consultant paediatrician (children's doctor). He had worked with polo neurological complications in the 1950's and developed a multidisciplinary team by the time children were being born with server *Thalidomide* harms. This took his work into supporting the Lady Hoare Memorial Trust in the 1960's, where a special unit became the focus for children with disabilities and multiple challenges. Following this in retirement post 1975 he worked for the *Thalidomide* Trust and in 1976 was awarded an O.B.E. [20].

Lady Hoare's work for Thalidomide survivors was a beacon of light for humanity, with her spirited endeavours being far ahead of both drug companies, and governments responsible for unimaginable harm. Lady Hoare did not have any of the agendas of procrastination or cover up, she simply acted compassionately and humanly by speaking up and acting in the best ways she could to highlight the plight of *Thalidomide* survivors.

Dr Quibell probably wrote the only enlightened report, out of a sense of public duty, knowing what he was seeing from years of medical experience was more than had been accounted for. He was right, but such healthy transparency was not permitted by the establishment, thus regrettably it did not result in the outcomes that it should have. Leaving the pertinent questions; why was this report not published, and why did the Alan Marre Report 1978 [12] not reflect this? Why has it taken a further 40 years and *"16 Weeks and Everything After..."*© to shine daylight onto this inaction?

Was this a cross institutional arrangement between big drug company pressures and bio-symbiotic complicity within the state? One thing is for certain, and that is there has been a long downward spiral of *Thalidomide* miss presentations originating from some very dark and sinister places.

Some even allege from passed on accounts that *Thalidomide* itself came out of the darkest days [21] of Nazi eugenic experiments on humans. Martin Johnson the now the former Director of TTUK appears to have had an ongoing curiosity with potential *Thalidomide* links to the Nazi era. In Harold Evans film *"Attacking the Devil – The last Nazi War Crime"* he suggests possible historical origins of *Thalidomide* to this era, but how much these can be fully substantiated today remains to be seen.

Harold Evans was one of the leading investigative journalists during the 1960's and 1970's. His work made significant insights into what had happened and what had gone wrong, helping gain recognition and acknowledgment for many of the more severely harmed *Thalidomide* people. His vigorous campaigns and digging for real information has provided key points highlighted in this book *"16 Weeks and Everything After..."©*.

"Attacking the Devil – The last Nazi War Crime", has its place in acknowledging all *Thalidomide*, harm inflicted on the unborn over the years, and potential links back to 1940's. This includes all who may have been harmed after 9 weeks and later on in pregnancy. Going forward nonetheless it would also be constructive and more likely to promote wider complete social justice, by transparently acknowledging all the people who have been harmed by *Thalidomide* in all stages of pregnancy, not only the first 9 weeks. This is both in the 1950's, 1960's across the western world and in developing countries since, yet these wrongs continues to remain ignored and unrecognised.

Thalidomide has been a long downward spiral from its origins to the present day

Despite some interesting and notable points, *"Attacking the Devil – The last Nazi War Crime"*, sadly did not come out and confront the myth of *Thalidomide* harm being restricted to only some days within a limited '9 week sensitive period'. Regrettably it appeared to stick to the on message narrative created and perpetuated by the *Thalidomide* establishment for the last 50 years.

It was particularly disappointing because instead of complete transparency, some weasel spin also appeared to be subliminally implanted that propped up the errant and incoherent limitations of the neural crest theory/hypothesis. Martin Johnson, the now former director of the *Thalidomide* Trust UK, but still leaving the impression of remaining on message, uses the line; *'precision of a snipers rifle'* when describing how *Thalidomide* affects the unborn. The semantics are significantly misleading as it implies only limited affects are possible during a handful of days within the first 9 weeks of pregnancy; the on message but errant flawed position of the *Thalidomide* settlement bodies for the last 50 years.

The above is a grossly confusing and wayward sound bite when considering *Thalidomide's* overall potential to cause damage and harm at all stages of pregnancy, in pre and embryonic stage (up to the first c.9 weeks), plus potentially all of the foetal stage (c.9-40weeks). A far more accurate and transparent metaphor would be; *"a wretched indiscriminate multiple dirty cluster bomb attack"*, leaving some more affected than others, but **all** violated over their entire lives', and **all** totally unnecessarily harmed regardless of or level of harm at any stage of pregnancy.

Harold Evans during his time at the Sunday Times during the 1960's and 1970's was a key person on the Investigational Team that achieved great progress in bringing to light many of the issues of *Thalidomide*, and the poor conduct of the government and drug companies. The Sunday Times Investigational Team had been silenced for about a decade due to ongoing legal proceedings of one sort or another, by the then terms of subjudicy. However when limitations became lifted, The Sunday Times Investigational Team published in 1979 Suffer the Children [2], revealing some of what had been concealed.

This was only during the year after the Alan Marre Report of 1978 that ignored such concerns and instead sided with the flawed neural crest theory/ hypothesis backed by the drug companies, governments and settlement bodies. Findings by the Sunday Times Investigational Team led by Harold Evans revealed evidence of significant contradictions to the flawed neural crest theory/ hypothesis. This came from work by Jurrand, Dr Poswillo and others evidencing vascular and antiangiogenesis based causations of *Thalidomide* harm [2, p343] [19], at complete odds to the errant on message position of the *Thalidomide* establishment had been claiming for by then over 15 years.

It was therefore depressing to sense Harold Evans usual savvy objectivity appeared to be over ridden by the *Thalidomide* establishment as their erroneous time frame limitations of *Thalidomide* harm subtly infiltrated the film; *"Attacking the Devil – The last Nazi War Crime"* in 2016. Lamentably the film also somehow failed to mention harms on the unborn from *Thalidomide* occur by the action of antiangiogenesis, and consequently harm and scale of risk to the unborn throughout pregnancy is greatly extended. Antiangiogenesis was confirmed beyond any doubt, evidently overlooked since the 1960's and widely in the public domain since 2009 [15]. Inherent contradictions the

Thalidomide Trusts and settlement bodies would have been very aware of, but strangely continue to remain notably silent on, in an ongoing state of amnesia resulting from 50 years of self indoctrination by their own propaganda. It appears easier today to simply publicly ignore such inconvenient facts, but instead continue to use P.R. spin to side step in a dismissive way as has been the case since the 1960s.

At the same time links did exist to the very darkest of places, from key personnel with very sinister and menacing Nazi pasts, through senior positions held at Grünenthal during the 1950's, 1960's and even into the 1970's. Former Nazi scientists included Otto Ambros [22] [23] [24], known as the 'devils chemist' and Dr Heinrich Mückter, who was a Nazi war criminal with a sickening history of horrendous experimentation on human beings. Worse still Grünenthal appointed Dr Mückter Head of science [20], and then incentivised him to sell as much *Thalidomide* as possible. Mückter received a constant salary of 14,400 German Marks. The first year in 1957, Mückter was rewarded with a 160,000 German Marks bonus, and by 1961 this had risen to 325,000 German Marks, a staggering twenty-two times his salary [1, p36-p37]. The average low paid worker's wage may have been around one sixth of a highly paid director's salary, without bonuses. Today Mückter's bonus would be equivalent (at 1960's rates) of c. $10,000 a week or c. ½ a $Million per year for poisoning and harming hundreds of thousands of unborn babies, plus inflicting adults with polyneuritis conditions.

Miss-presentation of information concerning *Thalidomide* is a long running theme, revealed over years of enquiry for this book. One discovery for me was particularly chilling, given it was in the year before my mother was given Distaval/*Thalidomide*. Dr Hendrick Mückter, Nazi war criminal and head scientist at Grünenthal [22] [23] personally researched and published a paper on the anti-cancer properties of *Thalidomide* [25]. Dr Mückter's 1965 study showed at least temporary anti-cancer properties of *Thalidomide* [25]. Available from the British library, it cost me a little over £20 to get a copy, and yet somehow has been hiding in plain sight for 50 years.

Get your facts first; Then you can distort them as you please [26]

Mark Twain

The results may not have provided enough to claim a permanent cure for cancer, but did evidence the extraordinary significance that *Thalidomide* killed cancer cells. What this meant must not be understated. Any drug capable of killing living cells is extremely likely to kill cells trying to develop throughout all stages of gestation. Even a temporary exposure has the undeniably obvious potential to kill cells of developing human life at all stages of pregnancy. For a developing baby such affects will not be temporary, as these cells can never go back and develop again, leaving the developing baby harmed for a life time, if they even survive through to birth?

In 1965 when Dr Hendrick Mückter made these findings it had been known for at least 15 years, any drug with anticancer properties could damage developing babies during pregnancy [3, p175] [1, p217]. But Grünenthal continued to deny any risks from *Thalidomide* on the unborn [3, p209-p210], and made no effort to alert the world to the clear transferable risks from even temporary anti-cancer properties of *Thalidomide* consumption during pregnancy.

In 1966 Mückter together with Moré produced a startling claim *Thalidomide* in a large dose could actually cause tumours [2, p361]. Would people exposed to *Thalidomide*, mothers and babies have an increased risk of cancer? My mother died of cancer, was *Thalidomide* a factor? Has *Thalidomide* taken in pregnancy years later led to cancers in mothers and or their offspring? How much would that have cost the NHS?

Although subsequent research has been less conclusive, and may relate to dosage etc, however no public safety warnings or safety acknowledgments were made by Grüthenthal. Regardless of any nuances' of the two above slightly conflicting studies whether *Thalidomide* killed developing cells at lower doses or promoted uncontrollable growth at larger doses, is irrelevant as far as the absolute responsibility to advise the public of real risks throughout pregnancy. Instead during 1966, before during and after I was being subjected to *Thalidomide* manufactured by Grüthenthal in Distaval tablets, Grüthenthal continued to promote misleading articles in national publications to suggest the safety concerns regarding *Thalidomide* were hysterical [27, p87].

More generally it had been known for years by the 1950's and 1960's drugs could cause problems for developing offspring, if taken during pregnancy [1, p217]. In 1939 Dr Speert tested sulphanilamide on rats and noted how litter size and birth weights dropped, and as a result he advised extreme caution for use in women who were pregnant, and not to use it if at all possible [1, p214].

In 1943 whilst running tests for quinine to combat malaria, Dr Francis Kelsey discovered rabbits' offspring were being harmed because they couldn't process the drug even though the mother rabbits could [27]. Dr Kelsey described how her learning had become; – *"Particularly conscious of the fact that the foetus or newborn may be pharmacologically an entirely different organism from the adult"* [28] [29]. This led to Dr Kelsey at the F.D.A. having grave concerns on learning *Thalidomide* caused side effects in adults of poly/ peripheral neuritis. Her concerns grew on learning this had not been disclosed to her at the F.D.A.; this resulted in the F.D.A. blocking a US licence until they could prove *Thalidomide* did not harm developing offspring. Nonetheless the *Thalidomide* drug companies knew poly/ peripheral neuritis side effects were occurring on an industrial scale [3, p59-p65, p113-p121]. It was also known drugs with a molecular mass under 1000 could pass through the placenta and on to the developing baby, and the molecular mass of *Thalidomide* is only 258 [5, p12]. Yet this is not how the *Thalidomide* drug companies presented things in the 1960's or any time since, as a strange state of amnesia subsequently descended.

"We cannot solve our problems With the same thinking that created them" [30]

Albert Einstein

D'Amato made a search in the early 1990's for a drug capable of acting as an inhibitor of angiogenesis; i.e. a drug causing antiangiogenesis [31]. He had made a library review of various drugs with antiangiogenesis properties and considered potential use for other purposes of a drug capable to impair blood vessel development in a growing foetus. D'Amato was stunned and taken aback to discover *Thalidomide* was top of the list. This was a strange cognitive dissonance type contradiction, to the medical profession and drug companies continued claim that Thalidomide harms on the unborn were due a mysterious nerve attacking neural crest theory/ hypothesis. However in 1994 D'Amato conducted tests to show a metabolite of *Thalidomide* did indeed produce effects of antiangiogenesis on the egg yolk [31] [5, p145-p148].

Trent Stephens worked together with one of his students Teresa Strecker on *Thalidomide* research from 1978 to 1983. She devised an intelligent procedure to physically block nerve development within the limbs of chicks by use of implanting a foil within the bone. Yet the chick bones still continued to grow without help from the nerves, revealing significant flaws in the neural crest theory/ hypothesis, as its central tenants were clearly wrong [5, p166]. This would have followed the Sir Allan Marre Report in 1978 [12] that had expediently fallen into line with the drug companies and their settlement bodies' narratives based on the errant neural crest theory/ hypothesis. Objective and constructive errors in methodologies of assessments of recognition criteria were dismissed by the panel on the Sir Allan Marre Report 1978, despite compelling contradictions to the status quo. Consequently a large cognitive dissonance persisted concerning the implications of *Thalidomide* antiangiogenesis on the unborn.

However in 2009 Dr Neil Vargesson at Aberdeen Medical Sciences demonstrated antiangiogenesis is indeed responsible for loss of limbs when *Thalidomide* exposure coincides with the limb budding stage [14]. Since then more work has put beyond doubt that the harmful action of *Thalidomide* is and always was antiangiogenesis. The significance of antiangiogenesis to harm developing babies goes far wider and beyond the budding stage; i.e. if limbs remain incomplete then the limb development is impaired or halted at the time point of exposure, e.g. weeks 10, 14, 19. In my case it was weeks 16, hence my arms and legs only developed up to c.85% as is the case at the 16th week stage of foetal development. The negative effects in my brain are commensurate in terms of physical development, but here the utility and functional loss is more like the reciprocal, i.e. not only a c.15% reduction in function, but more like a loss of c.85% impairment in specific areas that would otherwise have fully developed.

The contents in this chapter are most likely only a tiny fraction of a much larger untold account, i.e. the tip of the tip of the iceberg. For example Dr Heinrick Mückter on behalf of Chemie Grünenthal advised Dr Svedin of Astra Co. Sweden that test records and all the original test protocols prior to 1959 had disappeared during a move [3, p188-p190].

A more likely explanation may come from knowing the following. During 1966 a tip off and some luck enabled German Police to make raids on a secret bunker, for a primary court hearing in Aachen. Grünenthal held secret archives in this bunker, but information went missing before the raids on behalf of investigators for the prosecution [3, p209] [5, p23-24]. It's hard not to wonder if this might have contained the data and information concerning how *Thalidomide* killed animals and harmed humans [1, p96-100, p136]; plus clinical feedback on over 1500 known cases of very bad peripheral neuritis sensitization that somehow got misplaced too [5, p41]. Grünenthal secret archive/ store had been held underneath an old factory chimney [3, p46-p47], thus it probably isn't too difficult to guess what most likely happened to any incriminating documentation.

A garden path all the way down to the compost bin

The *Thalidomide* history of misinformation has long been a case of forgotten or strange science, and then being led up a corporate garden path.

"It's been gold, (NO!) just enough glitter Amongst the chicken feed, to give the impression of gold" (32)

'Smilie'

Tinker Tailor Soldier Spy © (2011) Studio Canal Ltd

17

Some Help from April fools

It was late afternoon and already dark outside, on a wet squally winter day in December 2010. Stepping into the dry and warmth of the local library I paused at the newspaper table to scan the day's headlines. One story was prominent, the end of the Harrier Jump Jet. Apparently the plane had been under review in the month leading up to the General Election on 31st March 1966, but thereafter was taken forward from April 1st by the re-elected Labour government. An announcement was made over the library's loudspeaker advising there was five minutes before closing time, but I continued to contemplate the date of April 1st 1966 [1]. It was a Friday, and the last week day at the end of weeks 20 of my mother's pregnancy, and therefore quite likley the final day of my exposure to Distaval/ *Thalidomide*. The realisation produced random thoughts of how my entire formed existence from before birth had coincided with the life time of the Harrier Jet. It instantly struck me as ironic, because in all the years and decades since, more had been revealed to the public about the secrets of the military Jet than the drug Distaval/ *Thalidomide*. A bit of a paradox as it was part of a cold war defence package supposedly to defend the freedoms of the Western world, and to protect a more open and free society; or so we were led to believe.

More ironic still was how Western governments completely overlooked the potential for the cold war to have been lost due to *Thalidomide*.

Richardson-Merrell Inc together with Chemie Grünenthal had already distributed 2.5 million Kevadon/ *Thalidomide* tablets as part of their *'Investigational Program'*, just before and around the time of the Cuban missile crisis. There was a further 10 million tablets waiting in the wings, to go out as an over the counter (O.T.C.) drug as soon as a licence was gained, with plans to step up production with immediate effect [2, p99-p100]. Perceived as a universal panacea for everything [3, p41], such levels of O.T.C. *Thalidomide* dissemination would have caused inconceivable levels of human harm, not to mention unimaginable financial and social costs for the USA.

A notable feature in the 1960's was how the East did not have the increasing numbers of babies being born with malformations compared to the West. The former Eastern Germany (G.D.R.) was completely free from the huge rise in babies born with malformations and impairments, and it was free from *Thalidomide*. Some raised the notion the increase in new babies with malformations was due to a virus, or radiation, but neither would stop at *'Check point Charlie'*, even if the border guards could and did stop people and most other things. Something pointed out by Dr Lenz at the start of German *Thalidomide* legal proceedings [4, p225].

The Minister for Health in the UK form 1960 to 1963 was Enoch Powell [2, p11]. In this position he had overall responsibility for the NHS, while considerable quantities of *Thalidomide* was given out under various brand names (about seven), and all marketed as *"Completely safe"* and *"atoxic"* [5 a-d]. Doctors had been erroneously advised *Thalidomide* was *"Completely Safe"* to prescribe and use on patients, including pregnant women, and at all stages of pregnancy including labour [6, p130, p134]. Distillers Company

Bio-chemicals Ltd referred to it as *"a proven remedy"* [7, p313].

Even more errant under the watch of Enoch Powell's term as Minister for Health's with responsibility for the NHS, *Thalidomide* was unbelievably reintroduced into hospitals post "withdrawal" from the wholesale market in 1962 up to the end of the year [6, p139]. Yet even worse, for the month after the supposed "withdrawal", Distillers Company Bio-chemicals Ltd continued in synchrony to advertise and promote *Thalidomide* as a safe drug [6, p14]. All this muddied the waters leaving the medical world unclear as to the level and extent of potential risks of *Thalidomide* on the unborn. Confusions only wrongfully confirmed supposed studies by Dr Ray Nulsen in Ohio claiming no risks existed when used in later pregnancy [8]. This had helped create the illusion of safety throughout pregnancy, despite that most likely two babies died and three were born with malformations from *Thalidomide,* during these clinical interventions, but somehow not reported at the time [3, p43].

On March 5th 1962 (four years to the week before my expose to *Thalidomide*) Mrs Joyce Butler asked the Minister for Health what action he was taking to ensure all new drugs were submitted to immediate and reliable scrutiny before use in the NHS? Enoch Powell Minister for Health replied, *"I have no power to do this"* [6, p142]. The answer to such hollow and dumb comments from Enoch Powell is another question, *"...If not the Minister for Health...then who does?"*

A delegation representing *Thalidomide* survivors had tried approaching the Minister for Health, but no response was forthcoming. By January 1963 they went in person, but Enoch Powell still refused to entertain even the possibility of considering a single aspect of any of their concerns. Enoch

Powell was reported to have said the following: [7, p314]

- No to a public enquiry
- No to the immediate setting up of a drug testing centre, only condemning *"anyone who takes an aspirin puts himself at risk"*. [These comments reduced the significance of risk from *Thalidomide* to that of only an aspirin, but the reality was aspirin was a much less toxic drug. At the time Distaval/*Thalidomide* had been perceived as a common analgesic, hence the comparison to aspirin; and another reason why so little record keeping was ever made in relation to Distaval/*Thalidomide* prescriptions.]
- No to giving a public warning against using any of the pills (*Thalidomide* tablets) out in wider society, not even within people's homes; any such warning Enoch Powell described as a, *"Scaremongering stunt"*
- No to giving a public statement afterwards; Enoch Powell stated, *"No need to bring the press into this"*
- No to even setting his eyes on a child with malformations caused by *Thalidomide* [7, p314]

At all stages of the *Thalidomide* disaster; before, during and after The Minister for Health's actions plus inactions were inadequate or worse, and failed to put public safety and wellbeing as the primary concern. Despite Enoch Powell's coldness and complete lack of compassion, he was more rattled than he was trying to let on [3, p80-p81]. Powell's put down to the *Thalidomide* parent's delegation who visited him in January 1963, was, *"I hope you're not going to sue the Government for damages; No one can sue the government"* [2, p190]. But this only confirms how deeply concerned he was about the government being sued, [3, p80-p81] and points to the real reason for declining a public enquiry.

'Power corrupts,
Absolute power corrupts absolutely'

Anon

The Minister for Health, Enoch Powell and Distillers Company Bio-chemicals Ltd top executives/ representatives frequented the same circles. Dr Walter Kennedy worked as a medical advisor for Distillers Company Bio-chemicals Ltd, but he had also previously worked for the Government as the Chief Medical Officer [2, p183-p191]. Enoch Powell liaised with Distillers Company Limited before he went on national Television concerning the issue of *Thalidomide*, and afterwards he requested their feedback. It smacked of an unhealthy level of cronyism. Enoch Powell informed Parliament and the nation on television *Thalidomide* was properly tested by Distillers according to the *"standards of the time"*. This implied nobody previously thought a drug could cross the placenta and reach the developing baby.

However all such notions were wildly misleading, as since the mid 1950's it had been known drug molecules sized at less than 1000 could pass through the placenta. In addition it was known *Thalidomide's* molecule was only 258, i.e. about one quarter the size known to pass the placenta [3, p12]. However this was not at the time reported in the press including notable publications like The Economist, The Times, The Manchester Guardian and The Sunday Telegraph.

April 1st 1966 was at the end of week 20 in my mother's pregnancy and the end of my Distaval/*Thalidomide* exposure. It was the same day Jack Ashley became elected M.P. for Stoke-on-Trent, South [9, p124]. He went on to be the one M.P. above all others who challenged and fought back against the *Thalidomide* drug companies, and went on to raise the profile of disability issues more widely. Initially Jack Ashley began in social policy, seemingly tipped for a mainstream Ministerial position. However this didn't happen in the first cabinet reshuffle [9, p134]. As a result he decided to resolve an issue with his hearing. Regrettably the operation went badly wrong, leaving him effectively totally deaf. Jack Ashley's plans for a return to Parliament were left in ruins, and in a quiet personal crisis he drafted his resignation letter [9, p136-p137].

Jack Ashley's departure was first reported by Stoke-on-Trent local press, but news travelled to London where wide support soon grew for him to continue as an M.P., and take on a new role promoting disability. With considerable commitment from his wife Pauline, he took up the role and became a constant reminder in Parliament of the needs of people with a disability, challenging pre-assumptions and stereotypes. At this point M.P. Jack Ashley in his new role championed the neglected *Thalidomide* Children, and many whose parents were in real need of basic practical day to day support and assistance. They had struggled on, but had been neglected by both government and the *Thalidomide* drug companies responsible [7, p313, p318].

"History doesn't always repeat itself, But it usually rhymes" [10]

Mark Twain

As in if Déjà Vous, Gordon Brown's Government in 2009 decided to tax benefits paid to *Thalidomide* people recognised by the legacy settlement body (*Thalidomide* Trust UK) of Distillers Company Ltd of the 1960's and 1970's [7, p336]. This represented some but not all of the people who were affected by the drug. Yet again Jack Ashley made a stand for *Thalidomide* survivors who the system had recognised, and called on the state to act on its responsibilities. But the then Minister for Health Alan Johnson, risked emulating Enoch Powell who held the same Office 50 years earlier, and initially said he was; *"not persuaded"* of a case for financial aid. This was for even the limited number of people Distillers Company (Bio-chemicals) Ltd acknowledged as being negatively impacted by *Thalidomide*, and who had a growing gap at the time of inadequate funds estimated at £160 million. However in the end an improved deal was arranged, for people with *Thalidomide* harms that the establishment chose to recognise.

By 2009 The Distillers Company Ltd no longer existed, but with mergers and takeovers morphed into the descendant entity Diageo. Diageo is a corporate superpower, the world's largest beer, and spirits Company. Together with the UK Government they made a further settlement around 2010. Diageo appear to have operated good corporate social responsibility conduct, and in general have paid out fairly for recognised UK and Australian *Thalidomide* survivors. However this has done nothing for unrecognised *Thalidomide* survivors who were harmed outside and beyond the mythical limited 9 week sensitive period; and in some cases slightly beyond where the corporate cognitive dissonance has allowed the myth to remain intact.

With no tribal allegiances left or right (whatever that really means), and being as politically disenfranchised as the next person I retain a very healthy scepticism of all in the political classes. Nonetheless as far as leaving no stone unturned on the untold account of *Thalidomide* and Machiavellian residual misinformation it seemed reasonable to visit my local M.P. In 2011 this happened to be Conservative Rt. Hon. Harriet Baldwin of Prime Minister David Cameron's Coalition Government.

Following my meeting with Rt. Hon. Harriet Baldwin M.P. it would be fair to say was proactive up to a point concerning the *Thalidomide* issues I raised. Harriet Baldwin M.P. probably did as much as anyone who was well meaning, but part of the establishment could or would be expected to have done. Disappointingly the human rights organisation Liberty did even less, despite the clear violation of the Right to Life. Ironic as Liberty's bias to favour international issues above and over UK ones, ignored how *Thalidomide* was on sale in Iran during 1966 [11], plus *Thalidomide* has continued to bring harm on the unborn since the 1960's in developing countries and even in Europe.

Rt. Hon. Harriet Baldwin M.P. fielded things wider, to Andrew Lansley and Kenneth Clarke who passed things on to the Department of Health, the Parliamentary Under Secretary of state for Quality (Lords), Earl Howe. But they too didn't offer any new insights into the issues I was seeking to have put out into the open, only managing to stick to the establishment mantra of the status quo. However none of that accounts or explains the affects and bio-marker legacy in me due to Distaval/*Thalidomide* exposure at weeks 16 to 20 of pregnancy. The same applies for others affected between weeks 9 and 16 plus even beyond weeks 20, but still not yet acknowledged.

The above feedback included how Medicines and Healthcare products Regulation Agency (M.H.R.A.) advised of a pregnancy screening programme was now in place. M.H.R.A. is strongly based on E.U. format and protocols; hence these may change in view of Brexit. However E.U. links raises some serious questions. Why has more not been done for *Thalidomide* survivors in Europe, and especially Spain given their place within the E.U. since the 1980's? The E.U. claims to hold a higher moral purpose, and therefore it is way over time to see the E.U. demonstrate it is not subservient to big corporations at the cost of wellbeing to its citizens. This includes taking action to fully and satisfactorily redress all those affected in all EU countries no matter what stage of pregnancy they were affected or what year they were harmed.

The UK likewise, and together with the German Government have a moral imperative to work together for all *Thalidomide* survivors, including those still not recognised and those neglected for decades in all countries. This may provide a valuable blueprint for tackling legacy issues in general, including all other drugs that may not have received adequate safe guards, scrutiny or retrospective redress.

At the time of writing UK Prime Minister is Theresa May and German Chancellor is the Angela Merchel. Individually and collectively from their time in office, they have a great opportunity to achieve a lasting maternal legacy, by standing up for unborn babies and their mothers. Andrea Merchel is affectionately known in Germany as *"Mutti"* (Mummy). Hence therefore something one would like to think as women would be very high on both their political agendas; assuming they really value and appreciate the significance and importance of issues relating to pregnancy and being a mother?

The German First Minister is Angela Merchel. She grew up in the former Eastern Germany, and therefore would have been spared the potential risk of being harmed by *Thalidomide*. However UK Prime Minister Theresa May, could so easily have been exposed to *Thalidomide* during her mother's pregnancy; including in her 16th week of gestation, because her mother needed a headache tablet, or a sedative, or day time hypnotic, or anti stress drug, or even late morning sickness tablet like my mother. An event that had it occurred would have ended Theresa's chances of ever succeeding to become UK Prime Minister, even from before being born.

All the same one would expect in the event of a change of Prime Minister regardless of gender or party, the same would apply. Today UK and German Governments need to work together to confront moral liabilities arising from April fool's day in 1960. Distillers Company Bio-chemicals Ltd did not produced the *Thalidomide* active ingredient, but instead imported it direct from Grünenthal as part of the original 1957 contract. From April 1st 1960 the two companies agreed to continue the arrangement. This provided a financial windfall for Grünenthal, and Germany, but also meant all *Thalidomide* products produced by Distillers Company Bio-chemicals UK Ltd were made using *Thalidomide* manufactured in Germany [12, p233]. Hence my mother was consuming, and I was therefore directly harmed by *Thalidomide* made by Grünenthal in Germany, throughout the month of March right up to the end of weeks 20, April 1st 1966.

Today both UK and German governments' legacies from former times require some genuine atonement for significant errors of judgment, concerning the full extent of the *Thalidomide* disaster and its aftermath. The obvious call

My last day of **Distaval**/ Thalidomide and the first day of a new
parliament

is for them to work together in an open and transparent
way, and for all sides to go for the moral high ground. It
would be good in general to create a more reflective tone
and tenor for drug companies' future conduct, especially
for where retrospective actions are required for previous
error for all drugs that have lingering question marks.

UK drug safety post Brexit has a moral duty to lead the
way, regardless of whether or not E.U. standards continue
to remain inadequate. The M.H.R.A. advice was said to
exclude *Thalidomide* from use at any stage in pregnancy,
and that is a good thing. However further transparency
is still required to explain the full facts and potential time
lines for harm during pregnancy, and how analogues
of *Thalidomide* may also have the same affects. These
have continued to be wrongly reported and assessed for
over 50 years. Consequently medical, pharmacological
and biological text books remain based on flawed and

inaccurate assumptions, for a new generation of medics and pharmacology professionals to unwittingly be indoctrinated with the same old misinformation. Not to mention, existing generations that have been misinformed.

Where doctors have been educated in the UK, or E.U., or other countries and then go on to work elsewhere in the world, any lingering misinformation will be taken with them. In developing countries and places where enforcement may not be as rigours or well observed, plus where a treatment may potentially be used in different ways or for different applications in the future, then wrongful assumptions of safety would hold future unsuspected risks of harm.

In Germany after the end of WW2 following the trial of *"The Twenty-Three"* Nazi doctors, the Nuremberg Medical Code was drafted. This was to ensure no patient would be used as a guinea pig without giving consent and any experiment would have to declare openly and transparently what animal tests had been done, and the results [3, p43-p44]. *Thalidomide* use in all countries could be described as amounting to a moral breach and violation of the Nuremberg Medical Code of the ethics on an industrial scale. Ironic given that such an important medical code drawn up in Germany appears to have been so fragrantly ignored by a German company, and seemingly let off the hook by successive German governments.

Today nationally and internationally the political class need to step up to the plate, and overturn the divide and rule strategies of the past, plus come clean on all aspects of drug safety during pregnancy. M.P.s elected to Parliament on April 1st 1966 and those elected before and since, have brought mixed and incomplete results for resolving all *Thalidomide* issues and other drugs taken in pregnancy with serious lingering question marks. Nonetheless Rt. Hon Jack Ashley led the way and ensured they hadn't all been April Fools.

Jack Ashley 1922 – 2012, Together with Pauline Ashley as interpreter achieved a real difference for the good

"16 Weeks and Everything After…" ©

PART V

Turning Negatives into Positives

18

A Heroine, plus Betsy Andreu's good example

Two women highlighted in this chapter provided insight and good example, choosing to do what was right, over and above taking easier options.

Dr Frances Oldham Kelsey, 24th July 1914 to 7th August 2015 A Heroine and Life saver

Dr Francis Kelsey by making a resolute stand against the dark forces of the powerful *Thalidomide* drug companies is perhaps the overall heroine above all others of the entire *Thalidomide* episode. Her qualities of courage, sincerity, objectivity and understated inner strength are again owed further acknowledgement.

In the early 1960's Dr Kelsey managed to prevent Richardson-Merrell in the US, working with Grünenthal of Germany, from gaining a licence for the drug *Thalidomide*. The scale of her success may be difficult to fully quantify, but her efforts prevented thousands of people from being seriously harmed by *Thalidomide*. It's best understood by realising what the drug companies' plans were had they got the green light for an over the counter (O.T.C) licence. An immediate 10 million Kevadon/ *Thalidomide* tablets would have flooded on to the US market around spring 1961 [1, [p99-p100], while new production would have been stepped up for the long term. In addition as a stock gap, 2½ to 5 million further tablets would also have been instantly produced [1, p100], as there was already enough pre-existing materials from surplus ingredients.

It has been said that had the *Thalidomide* licence not been stopped in the US, then additional financial strains and other complications may even have resulted in losing the cold war. Perhaps this is why President John F Kennedy paid particular attention. He swiftly gave a televised US press conference acknowledging Dr Kelsey's courageous work [2, p257] [3]; then awarded her the Distinguished Civilian Service Medal on August 7th 1962 [2, p246-p247]. President Kennedy's initial action ensured regulation changes were put in place. New procedures were implemented from around June to September 1966 in the US, with new antibiotic treatments that prevented further *'Investigational Programs"* and drug trials without first establishing efficacy [2, p247, p257, p347].

Canadian born Dr Frances Oldham married Dr F. Ellis Kelsey whilst in Chicago, and became a naturalised U.S. Citizen [3]. Together they worked in science, including studies funded by the US Government to protect soldiers' lives' against malaria using quinine. This research in the 1940's produced some pertinent and notable results in relation to the effects of quinine on pregnant rabbits. Dr Kelsey noted a mother rabbit's liver broke down quinine, but the foetus's liver was not capable of doing so. Consequently the drug stayed in the foetus's system much longer, and became toxic to the foetus, but not to the mother. The fact drugs crossed the placenta and were metabolised differently by developing offspring was a profound insight. This stayed with Dr Kelsey, who described how her learning had become; *"Particularly conscious of the fact that the foetus or newborn may be pharmacologically an entirely different organism from the adult"* [4] [5, p45].

On August 1st 1960 Dr Francis Kelsey began working for the F.D.A. [3, p6]. Only about six weeks later in September 1960 Richardson-Merrell submitted a licence application for their brand of *Thalidomide* known as Kevadon and coded as K17 [5, p17, p41]. They had joined forces with Grünenthal 18 months earlier and were in the final stages of bringing the drug to the Market. Dr Kelsey was given the responsibility of processing the *Thalidomide* application, because it was perceived to be an easy introductory task [3, p6].

Grünenthal and Richardson–Merrell had good reason to be optimistic for Kevadon/ *Thalidomide* to be licensed for sale in the US, as at the time following an application, the F.D.A. had only 60 days to decide the drug was unsafe for the proposed use. If the F.D.A. didn't respond by the end of two months it received automatic F.D.A. approval, plus there was no need of evidence of the drug's efficacy. Hence rejection by the F.D.A. had to be founded in hard data. Where there is no data forthcoming to challenge, it becomes extremely difficult, consequently the drug companies effectively held all the cards [5, p40].

The 'Clinical/ Investigational Program' was completely unknown to Dr Kelsey and the F.D.A. However Dr Kelsey was troubled by the supposed perfect credentials of *Thalidomide* claiming to be tremendously safe and offered excellent test results to the point where they were difficult to believe. Her husband Ellis Kelsey had expressed his disbelief of *Thalidomide*'s supposed L.D.50 (lethal dose in 50%) claim of no toxicity. Not least as no other substance can make this claim. Yet at the same time claims of

Thalidomide's potency was incredible as well as diverse, but the two opposing claims were clearly a contradiction [1, p104].

Dr Francis Kelsey corresponded with Richardson-Merrell on glowing test results for *Thalidomide;* stating *"no evaluation can be made of the safety of the drug when used for a prolonged period of time"* [5, p49]. Additionally the F.D.A. requested evidence rats were actually absorbing the drug and it was entering the bloodstream, and not simply being excreted [6, p115]. Yet considerable challenges sill remained for Dr Kelsey and her intuition that the drug was not safe, because *Thalidomide* would gain a licence by default. Nonetheless her actions bought some time and provided the F.D.A. with another sixty days [5, p49].

March 6th 1961 was the target date for Richardson-Merrell's market release of Kevadon/ *Thalidomide* in the US. Only days before on February 23rd 1961, Dr Kelsey spotted a copy of the British Medical Journal (BMJ) December 31, 1960 [7]. It arrived late due to a mail or shipping strike, as they were transported by sea and some time had passed since the original publication date. In an instant, one correspondence article p1954 written by Dr A. Leslie Florence in the UK provided a game changer.

The article, 'Is *Thalidomide* to Blame?' explained he had seen four patients who had taken Distaval, a brand of *Thalidomide*, and all displayed paraesthesia of the hands and feet, coldness of the extremities and nocturnal cramps in leg muscles [7]. For Dr Florence this seemed too much of a coincidence not to have a more significant and related connection to *Thalidomide*. Underlying these concerns, it was noted how and when people were taken off Distaval/ *Thalidomide*, a marked reduction of symptoms followed. However more serious was on ending *Thalidomide* use symptoms didn't always stop in all people who had taken the drug, strongly indicating *Thalidomide* could also cause serious sensitisation issues. [N.B. my belief is, my mother suffered these effects for the rest of her life at a mild level, but no connection was made to Distaval/ *Thalidomide*, as the issue remained undisclosed to me for nearer 40 years. I too sometimes have slight tingling in my hands, is this foetal sensitisation?]

Dr A. Leslie Florence clinical observations provided enough for Dr Kelsey to challenge the drug companies to provide better evidence and safety test results to F.D.A. standards. Unable to meet either prevented *Thalidomide* gaining a licence by default [6, p114-p116]. This was in a time when it was difficult for women to make such stands in male dominated worlds like the F.D.A.

It is profound how decades later in 2018, Dr Kelsey

Dr Kelsey said not to be taken during all of pregnancy and she was right

may yet still offer more evidence and information to assist unrecognised *Thalidomide* affected people. In an almost throw away piece of evidence, Richardson-Merrell and Grünenthal inadvertently gave away that *Thalidomide* was already being tested for anti–cancer properties in early 1962 [5, p54]. This is of very real significance, because the medical and pharmaceutical world had known for years not to ever use cancer drugs with women who were or could be pregnant.

In the event the F.D.A. has Dr Kelsey's correspondences, files and archives, then these may turn out to be very useful, concerning residual issues of *Thalidomide* over 50 years on. This would be relevant for people ignored and sidelined for decades by the *Thalidomide* drugs companies and inept governments concerning false timescale limitations of harm. *Thalidomide* survivors in Spain are one group in particular, with instances from the 1980's over 20 years after the supposed "withdrawal from the wholesale market" [8]. Other countries such as Italy and Brazil may have lingering issues for *Thalidomide* survivors in a wider sense, including people who have been negatively affected by *Thalidomide* outside the bogus limited 9 week sensitive period. Assistance from the F.D.A. would both continue and enhance a brilliant legacy left by Dr Kelsey, who in her quiet understated way, thwarted and prevented the most colossal human disaster.

"Tenacity; If you get up one more time than you fall, you will make it through."

Chinese Proverb

Betsy Andreu dared to challenge the powerful drug cheats in the sport of cycling and won

Betsy Andreu is acknowledged not concerning *Thalidomide*, but for her inspiring and spirited stand against injustice. Like Dr Francis Kelsey she stood alone against powerful corporate forces and a media otherwise blind to the relevant issues. Drug cheating in professional cycling enveloped big business, real estate, betting, sport governors and regulators, the press, banks/ financial institutions, sports clothing/ product and bike manufactures [9] [10].

Cycling had a different menacing form of drug misuse
(Photography support: two clean local cyclists acting the role of bad guys)

Betsy Andreu drew on her sound moral compass and demonstrated the courage required to speak out against corrupt practices in cycling, and then held her ground. Betsy Andreu was prepared to cite the *"Hospital Incident"*, based on a visit with Frankie Andreu to see Lance Armstrong while he was a hospitalised cancer patient. Recalling the visit Betsy asserted he disclosed of taking a wide range of performance enhancing substances, including, steroids, testosterone, and EPO (Erythropoietin).

Later this event was denied, but Betsy stood by the validity of the *"Hospital Incident",* and made a sworn Affidavit to defend her account. Despite being completely isolated Betsy became the last and only person prepared to testify on the *"Hospital Incident"* [11, p235].

Drug cheating and the scale of it in cycling, continued to remain veiled, but journalist Sir David Walsh sensed not all was well, in a way not unlike how Harold Evans from the Sunday Times challenged *Thalidomide* injustices. Sir David Walsh became convinced individual cycling performances were unrealistic, and sought ways to uncover wrong doing [10]. More doubts grew but large financial powers in cycling appeared to close ranks, and retained the upper hand [11].

However Betsy Andreu's sworn affidavit stood defiant against the undercurrent of falsehood, and eventually eleven former team mates of Lance Armstrong followed Betsy Andrea's lead. They too made sworn affidavits on her side, filed in a report by the US Anti-Doping Agency (USADA) witnesses for the prosecution, publically vindicating Betsy Andreu [9, p378-p380]. There was one last veiled attempt by the drug cheats ring leader to discredit her hospital account, but Betsy authentically challenged this on US TV [12], even though by then the public had seen enough to believe her sworn affidavit was the real account.

Wisdom within a sworn affidavit

Drawing on inspiration from Betsy Andreu, *"16 Weeks and Everything After..."©* is my sworn affidavit for The Court of Public Opinion, to bring to light and challenge the *Thalidomide* drug companies' underhand misinformation and falsehood spin dating back to the 1960s. In the event a formal sworn affidavit for real life proceedings is required, I would have no hesitation in recounting verbatim all key information in *"16 Weeks and Everything After..."©* that was leant a helping hand by both a Heroine, and Betsy Andreu's good example.

"My Story is that you can stand up to a bully. Don't let the bully win, never let the bully win." (13)

Bestsy Andreu

19

A Zeitgeist Lens for Action

King John, 1166 to 1216, reluctantly set his seal to a Charter during June 1215, in a summer meadow at Runnymede in Surrey, England [1].

King John 1166 to 1216 Worcester Cathedral

Articles of the Barons were transformed from a rough set of ideas and aspirations into an unambiguous legal form resulting in the Magna Carta. The Great Charter was compiled in 4000 words constructed out of deep Latin, and meticulously assembled onto a dried and smoothed parchment of sheepskin. Thirteen copies were produced and distributed across the realm.

Clauses 39 and 40, defines; life, liberty and property for whom an individual would be respected and rights be upheld [2]. Not long after, King John claimed he had been coerced by the Pope who had tried annulment of the Charter. King John died in 1216, and in accordance with his last wish was buried in Worcester Cathedral [1]. William Marshal was King John's loyal advisor, and together with the Archbishop Stephen Langton helped to revive the standing of the monarchy by reissuing the Charter immediately in 1216 and again in 1217; where it was split into *'Charter of the Forest'* and the *'Greater Charter'*. John's son, Henry III, issued the definitive version of the Charter in 1225 calling it his *'magna carta'* [1].

Some suggest the original Magna Carta document was signed under a 2500 year old yew tree that still lives close to the river Thames [3]. English Yew trees *(Taxus baccata)* never die, and as long as they are not destroyed they rejuvenate [4], symbolic of the Magna Carta spirit that continues to endure even if from time to time it requires some encouraging regeneration.

Law in the UK is divided between two types, civil and criminal law. Civil law differs significantly compared to criminal law as the standard of proof in tort is based on *'balance of probabilities', i.e. not absolutes.* The tort of lawsuit for example is brought by a claimant in a dispute between individuals and companies [5, p250]. The test for negligence requires establishing a breach of duty of care owed by the defendant resulting in harm being caused. No contractual relationship between the parties exists, although such claims can occur where a contract exists [5, p247].

An incident involving the decomposed remnants of a snail in a ginger beer bottle, which was unable to be seen through the dark glass, led to the case of Stevenson v Donoghue (1932). Mrs Donoghue drank the ginger beer and became very ill [5, p250]. Mrs Donoghue could not sue under the law of contract, due to the ginger beer having been purchased from her friend the retailer who didn't have the responsibility for the snail contaminating the beverage; and therefore had no contractual law obligation to her. The only legal action available to Mrs Donoghue was the tort of negligence. This enabled her to sue the manufacture of the ginger beer. It required demonstrating the burden of proof sided with her claim in three areas:

1. That the defendant (manufacturer of the ginger beer) owed the claimant a duty of care.
2. That the defendant was in breach of this duty.
3. That such actions by the defendant caused harm or injury to the claimant.

Mrs Donoghue was successful in her claim against the manufacture of the ginger beer under the tort of negligence, by passing the contractual relationships of the retailer [5, p250]. Stevenson v Donoghue (1932) became the bench mark ruling for the law of negligence through the duty of care principle. A wider rule in such cases was brought by Lord Atkin of the *'neighbour principle'*, or *'neighbour test'*. This puts the onus of duty of care on

The pertinent legacy of a former snail

anyone who could reasonably foresee acts or omissions would be likely to injure your neighbour [5, p250-p251]. Legally your *'neighbour'* is any person so closely and directly affected by my act that I ought to reasonably have them in contemplation as being so affected when directing my mind to the acts or omissions called into question [5, p250-p251].

This established precedent added to clarity over the years, to include reasonably foreseeable and sufficient proximity between parties in the wider sense, and fairness to impose a duty of care. Although Judges will not have to consider counter interpretations if a case falls within established categories of courts president for duty of care [5, p252].

The German *Thalidomide* trial started in Arldorf near Aachen, where the company owners and eight executives at Grünenthal were charged with criminal negligence and manslaughter. In 1970 all charges were dramatically dropped. Official reasons cited the defendants were of *"minor guilt"* and therefore offered *"no good public reason"*. Worse still the appalling court ruling protected Grünenthal defendant's immunity from further prosecution [6]. Today this needs to be seriously revisited and overturned for the interests of global justice.

Dr Hendrick Muckter head scientist at Grünenthal, and also a Nazi war criminal had already been given the luxury of getting out of jail around 15 years earlier, and in 1970 was excused for yet more atrocities on human beings. The German court acted to block people harmed by *Thalidomide* where the drug had been made outside Germany. This appeared to exclude all *Thalidomide* sold in other countries [7]. However around 2011/ 2012 Australian lawyer Michael Magazanik and his team made some startling discoveries, confirming all *Thalidomide* products sold by Distillers Company Bio-chemical's Ltd contained the active ingredient *Thalidomide* manufactured by Grünenthal in Germany [8, p233]. Thus it turns out the active ingredient *Thalidomide* made in Germany by Grüthenthal was the harmful ingredient in the Distaval tablets I was exposed to each day throughout March 1966. This evidence not previously acknowledged, now needs be considered for all its wider implications to more satisfactorily address issues brushed under the carpet for five decades.

Paul Whitworth Photography

It is essential to see history transparently

"Our lives begin to end the day we become silent about things that matter" [9]

Martin Luther King, Jr.

Grünenthal and their highly paid executive got away legally with a lot of wrong doing, and have never paid a commensurate sanction for the betrayal of trust against society. Injustices were in a style of operating a thousand years earlier pre Magna Carta. Yet legal precedent of Magna Carta was in place prior to 1970, and consequently in the case of *Thalidomide* it needs to re-instate legal obligations and rights in place prior to 1970. Seen through society's zeitgeist lens legal exemptions for *Thalidomide* drug companies had no right to be given in the first place. If required then the UK needs to lead the way as it did eight hundred years ago in 1215 to 1217.

Thalidomide survivors and their families have a history of being treated badly by the legal establishment since the 1960's. The *Thalidomide* drug companies, and governments concerned were financially much stronger and more powerful than families/ guardians of *Thalidomide* survivors, and were often not in a position to seek redress. Legal assistance individually and collectively was woefully inadequate, and again reminds society today of the importance of right to legal aid and access to challenge large corporations in general.

"Possession is nine tenths of the law"

Anon

"But being optimistic that still leaves, 1/10"

Paul 2017

Despite derisory legal aid and poor legal guidance, plaintiffs' claims against the drug companies and government had a much greater and stronger case than they were led to believe. The litmus indicator of the real legal rights and real legal potential for all *Thalidomide* survivors was obliquely revealed years later. Lloyd's of London had refused to increase an insurance settlement when some liabilities dramatically increased in the early 1970's for Distillers Company Ltd. This led in 1976 to insurers Lloyd's of London winning court proceedings in a dispute over the insurance claim. Distillers Company UK Ltd lost, because they had failed to carry out sufficient or adequate tests and research on *Thalidomide*; i.e. in effect it appears as tantamount to asserting Distillers Company

Ltd always had been legally liable for Negligence [10, p269]. By default this equally implicates Grünenthal likewise, and to a considerably greater extent.

Had there been satisfactory and commensurate financial backing for legal teams to ensure parity for plaintiffs compared to the asymmetric power and financial might of the *Thalidomide* drug companies and government side, then *Thalidomide* survivors would have much better legal outcomes. This would have brought about a much quicker resolution and would also have opened things up for a more transparent account. Most likely the airbrushing, misinformation and inadequate recall without satisfactory safety warnings for later pregnancy would have prevented events that led me to write this book.

Following the 1973 settlement it took a further three years to 27th June 1976, before restrictions finally got lifted on *'contempt'* of court that had muted what legal evidence still existed [10, p294-p313]. However by then it was around 14 years on, and *Thalidomide* issues didn't have the same public attention they had previously. In the intervening years the silence had allowed a great deal by then to drift off into history in exactly the way that the drug companies wanted.

Harold Evans of the Sunday Times investigational Team kept Marjorie Page and Elaine Potter working on investigation for a few further months. They concluded there always had been an excellent legal case waiting to be developed, if only the parent's legal teams had been more effective [11, p335]. As for preventing the Sunday Times reporting on the origins of the *Thalidomide* tragedy, using UK law of *'contempt'*, this was shown to be a breach of free speech under Article 10 of the European Convention for the Protection of Human Rights. Following this the UK

Government enacted a statutory reform to prevent the years of legal silence in the case of *Thalidomide* being repeated. This meant future reporting and comment would be permissible in civil litigations until a case was actually set down for trial [11, p335].

Lord Pearson revised legal precedents under the place of tort (locus delict) in relation to where something was produced but where the damage occurred elsewhere. Previous restrictions were dropped, meaning where the plaintiff suffers harm or damage does not matter in relation to where the product was made. This included both the direct or immediate damage providing the complete action in tort observed, as in the case of Distillers Co. (Bio-chemicals) *Ltd. v* Thompson [1971] AC 458 [12]. In this situation, Australia was the place where the plaintiff suffered damage from Distaval/*Thalidomide*, but it could relate to products from anywhere in the world, not only where it was manufactured. Distillers Company Ltd had tried to utilize a loophole by shipping *Thalidomide* from the UK in an almost completed state then labelling, or relabeling in Australia. This process enabled claiming the product had not been manufactured in Australia, and thus avoided relevant drug regulations. Yet paradoxically the *Thalidomide* tablets instantly became a completed product (Distaval) for sale, but enabling the claim of being produced in Australia, and thus avoided import regulations. Distillers Company UK Ltd held 933 shares out of 1000 in another company in Australia; either Distillers Company Australia Ltd [13], or possibly a third triangulated holding company to facilitate paperwork for the above described import process.

"All substances are poisons; there is none that is not a poison. The right dose differentiates a poison and remedy" [14]

Paracelsus, *'Father of toxicology'* (1493-1541)

Sometimes the only safe dose is ZERO, NILL, ZILCH, NOTHING applicable re; *Thalidomide* exposure on developing babies throughout all of pregnancy. It appears negligence in the case of Distillers Co. (Bio-chemicals) Ltd., v. Thompson (1971) AC 458 [12], was sought on the potential risks of harm during pregnancy. It related to omissions and the absence of safety warnings on the packaging of Distaval/ *Thalidomide*, as printed materials on and with the packaging conveyed general product safety. In effect this was seen as wrongly projecting implied safety claims.

The above aspects of the Australia 1971 case maybe highly relevant and applicable to my situation, i.e. No contra indications for use of Distaval/ *Thalidomide* beyond

Paul Whymark Photography ©

Old riffs can return with a fresh feel

9 weeks were made then or since, but instead continued bogus claims for safety in later pregnancy.

"The Emperor doesn't have any clothes"

Anon

("He never did")

Paul 2014

Many would say it is finally time Grünenthal and other *Thalidomide* drug companies faced the music. Perhaps the Beatles *"Get Back"* from 1968 the same year Grünenthal appeared in a German high court trial would be quite apt.

There may be more ways to apply pressure 50 years on and one avenue may offer potential through the use an unthought-of legal legacy. The *Thalidomide* drug companies appear to have been significantly remiss of their statutory health and safety obligations and duties. These existed in the UK during March 1966 under the Offices Shops and Workplace Act (OSRA) 1963 (1965 in Northern Ireland) [15]. Under OSRA 1963 obligations applied to ensure safety for the public (SECTION 1 to 4, and includes articles, chemicals and substances (SECTION 20), with no specified exclusions for pharmaceutical drugs. Section 1 states the premises the stature applied, and by implication included doctor's surgeries, pharmacies/ dispensaries', and all people who might visit the premises in the course of business. Not surprisingly this will cover all patients to the surgery including and perhaps in particular expectant mothers, and their developing babies with the implicit extra care required.

The drug companies were operating vicariously in such

premises; and therefore should owe vicarious liability through acts and omissions, of not warning of safety risks and hazards of the substances prescribed and obtained on said premises. As medics were acting in good faith, but misinformed by the drug companies they would not be liable. However NHS organisational liability is perhaps less clear cut, and would require further legal input.

In the Health & Safety at Work Act 1974 [16] under Section 9 duties of OSRA 1963 became incorporated, meaning further action would be implemented through the Health & Safety at Work Act 1974. It could be argued this strengthens the position as it points to a greater and extended implicit duty of care and obligation. My understandings are Health & Safety at Work Act 1974 action is more like civil law as assessments are deemed more in line with balance of probabilities, rather than absolutes. It may be on indictment there are potentially unlimited fines? Further details in this area may be contained in small print, and interpretations of Health & Safety at Work Act 1974 section 33.

Statutory law covers *'Strict Liability'* applicable where there is relevance for wider public good; for example in the case of *Alphacell v. Woodward* (1972), where an overflow setting in commercial paper-making process became blocked and resulted in polluted water being discharged into an adjacent river. Alphacell were operating pumps and process, so the fact the pump became blocked was immaterial as it was their responsibility to ensure failure of the system didn't negatively impact on the environment and others [5, p232–p233].

The statutory aspect indicators above could be helpful as OSRA 1963 obligations and duties were in place before the German courts 1970 intervention that let Grünenthal off the hook for further prosecutions of *Thalidomide* liabilities. One would like to think timelines of evading statutory duties owed in early 1966 has potential for future action.

In addition there may be more leverage through statutory legislation, as Freedom Of Information (F.O.I.) now extends to The Health and Safety At Work Act 1974 under section 28, [17] and this includes provision to include OSRA 1963, s59 coverage [15] [16]. The objective is to remove unnecessary barriers to openness in section 28 for public engagement/ participation in the process [17]. As a significant amount of information has historically been held back/ obscured or misrepresented it provides a great opportunity in the public interest for openness and gaining further and more rounded transparent disclosures.

To facilitate action today the UK Parliament may need to enable re-examination of old drugs given to pregnant women, and devise action and provision for where new information has come to light.

There may also have been possible regulation breach of the Code of Medical Ethics, evolving out of *"The Twenty-Three"* Nazi doctors at the Nuremberg Military Tribunal concluded in 1947 requiring consent from subjects/ participants [18, p109]. Not least as Head of Science and Research at Grünenthal Dr Hendirck Mückter was a known Nazi war criminal along with other senior directors at the time [6] [19].

It would be good to think *"16 Weeks and Everything After..."* © in some small way made a contribution towards wider and greater outcomes for justice in the style of Magna Carta: i.e. nobody including corporations, governments, or $/£/ € Billion drug companies are not even remotely the slightest bit above the law.

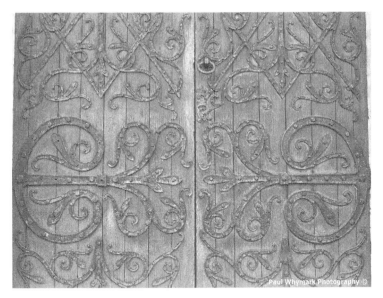

The far doors of Worcester Cathedral and the spirit of Magna Carta still live on

In the event the clock of time limitations is restarted it provides a great opportunity for strong able legal minds with inner steely qualities to take on the drug companies concerned, and win.

More possibilities may exist than has been previously considered for challenging the status quo. With public support it could help bring **all** the drugs consumed in pregnancy that continue to have lingering alleged question marks brought into the focus of a Zeitgeist lens for Action.

"To no one will we sell, To no one deny or delay right or justice" [20]

Magna Carta (1215): Clause 40

20

Knowledge Sharing

There is nothing new about fake news. A great deal has circulated for decades regarding the full extent of risk and harm inflicted from *Thalidomide* on developing babies, and continues even today.

Close attention is required not to miss the
critical detail
(Photography support: Barn Owl Centre,
Gloucestershire GL2 5LE)

This includes before the drug came to the market, during its time on the market and post "withdrawal" from the wholesaler. Counterfeit presentations have continued to be made to professionals and the public over the decades since, by the settlement bodies on behalf of the drug companies and expedient bio-symbiotic areas of the establishment.

"The most important thing in communication is hearing what isn't said" [1]

Peter Ducker

It wasn't only the science that got airbrushed, as historical and social accounts received the same underhand treatment. Gary Skyner a *Thalidomide* survivor and campaigner revealed how hospital staff called at his family's home in the 1960's to commandeer the packaging of the Distaval/*Thalidomide* tablets [2]; but his mother was strong enough to decline, and retained the packaging. Although it does leave the question where did such action derive from? Was it the UK Ministry for Health?

In 1962 Mr and Mrs Hudson of Yorkshire became parents to a baby who only survived for about 12 hours after birth, due to the severity of harm caused by *Thalidomide*. In an appalling addition of insult to injury, their babies' existence was then deleted, presenting the impression their baby never appeared to have existed. Other parents who lost babies due to *Thalidomide* became airbrushed out of official records. Birth and medical records had omissions, and information that went missing, then *Thalidomide* babies were buried in unmarked graves to perpetuate the silence, providing the impression the baby never even existed [3]. These events are yet more indicators of wider behind the scenes efforts to limit transparency. It implies this was occurring at more than one level and beyond the boundaries of more than one organisation/ institution. This same menacing feel is something at the edges I too have encountered during my personal journey over the last fifteen years, and probably without realising during my childhood hospital visits in the 1970's and 1980's.

The full impact of the social history of *Thalidomide*, along with areas the drug companies were directly responsible for, also extended to other institutions. Harold Evans has highlighted judicial/ political appointments in Germany around 1966 (probably at the time and soon after I was being directly affected by the drug), contributed to establishing a climate that ultimately protected Grünenthal from facing full liability [4]. Such reports strongly hint at how German government decisions of the late 1960's to 1970 let Grünenthal legally off the hook [4]. Reports have implied Grünenthal received some state funding, from the National German state (West Germany at the time) [5], during some of the time they developed/ sold *Thalidomide*. Assuming this was the case then it implicates the extent of German state responsibilities yet further. The UK government has no wiggle room either, as they too cannot be let off the hook for their errors and substantive poor practice made by UK ministers and officials, at the highest levels as reflected in Chapter 18 *"Some Help, from April Fools"*.

During my journey of both self discovery and learning of wider societal issues it became evident other drugs may have caused harmful effects on developing babies if taken during pregnancy, but still have not received adequate scrutiny. How many, and which other drugs may have harmed developing humans from even before conception, and during pregnancy over the years is hard to say.

Primodos is another drug with continued allegations and questions against it, from its use as a pregnancy testing drug. Primodos survivors and families feel they have not even had the (limited) level of recognition of *Thalidomide*.

With Primodos there appears some jarringly similar sounding contextual issues to *Thalidomide*, and both drugs became used for more than one specific purpose [6] [7]. Both *Thalidomide* and Primodos sardonically were drugs used to kill human cells. In the case of *Thalidomide* this was for killing detrimental or cancer type cells. While Primodos type compounds secondary use is as acerbically mocking as it is scarcely believable, with its dual persona being a morning after pill, intended to terminate pregnancy and any development of a baby.

Primodos was originally a drug produced by Schering, now owned by Bayer. In 2016 Bayer merged with Monsanto to work in genetic aspects of crops at both ends of the seed life cycle [8].

Findings by Jason Farrell and others on the Sky News team have shed some further light, on an unsatisfactory relationship between drug companies and regulators in the era 1965 to 1970 [7]. This goes back to the same time frame in early 1966 when my mother was given *Thalidomide* while pregnant with me, and advised it was completely safe. Both drug companies and governments appear to have disregarded and treated with contempt, mothers who took Primodos during pregnancy. The strong indication from Jasson Farrell's investigation into Primodos points to behind the scenes moves to limit transparency, similar to that of *Thalidomide* [6].

Strange as it may sound today, pregnancy testing at

one time would be made using a procedure of collecting a women's unrine sample, then injecting some of this urine into toads. In the event the woman was pregnant her urine would result in the toad producing eggs, and thereby indicate the woman who provided the urine sample was pregnant. Then in 1958 a new form of test using a tablet arrived in the form of Primodos from Schering, a German pharmaceutical company. Primodos utilized the powers of syntheic hormones, 5mg of Norethisterone and 0.01mg of ethinylostradiol. The premise was if a woman was not pregnant, then Primodos brought on a period but if she was pregnant then no period would occur [7].

Hormone based pregancy testing like Primodos was a very simlar chemical make up to the Morning After Pill, but about 13 times the strength, and about 40 times a contraceptive pill. Where health compliations and or malformations in children born following the use of Primodos it has been aledged harms resulted from the consumption of Primodos. Many would probably suggest given the dosage outlined above it would be strange if the compounds did not have some negative or terratogenitic affects.

By 1967 peditritian Dr Isabel Gal, had observed a troubling clinical pattern of babies born with spinal damage, and produced a study that found a high proportion of babies were born with spina biffida in mothers who had taken hormonal pregnancy testing drugs. Dr Gal published her findings in the scientific journal Nature, but her insights were not taken seriously by officials [6] [7].

Then in 1970 Primodos temporarily lost its liecence for use as a pregancy test, but somehow sarcastically the drug continued to be used. Primodos appears to have had an troubling set of events in its history, and holding of dual or multiple persona's. Five years later in 1975, and after who knows how many babies had been exposed, Primodos got a warning added to the packet; stating the drug *"May cause congential abnormaities"*. By 1977 The regulators sent another warning that the *"Association has been confirmed"*, and eventually in 1978 it was withdrawn from the market, eighteen years after pregnant women first began using it. The Sunday Times in 1978 asked the glaringly obvious question, why had it taken so long to remove the drug from the market? For those who allege Primodos caused harm on them or their offsping there has never been a full or satisfactory answer [6] [7].

Imagine a car dealer with a notice saying; *"the cars breaks and seat belts could* simultaneously *fail and this could mean uncontrollably crashing"*. Would you be happy travelling in that car, perhaps with your children in the back on a wet windy winter night along a twisting country road? Now imagine this same model has apparently crashed in a number of such circumstances, but with an inconclusive crash investigation report. Yet at the same time suggestions are may have been a problem with an electronic chip that controls both brakes and seat beat release systems. But don't worry, they say it has not been proven, and all the crashes were just bad luck. Now imagine with this background knoweldge, how you feel about being driven in one of these auto pilot cars, because others have the power to decide?

Dr Gall tried for more than ten years to stop the use of hormonal prengancy drug testing, and had sought funding to establish further evidence to back up her inital findings. A battle resulted between the Department of Health along with the Safety of Drugs Committie. Dr Gall in particluar fought the Senior Medical Officer for the Safety of Drugs Committie, Dr William (Bill) Inman who chose to disregard Dr Gall's clincal findings. Yet strangely Dr Inman destroyed his own evidence indicating a 5:1 chance of malformtion/prebirth damage from Primodos, to stop others using it for legal action [7].

A lot of unanswered questions are left concerning open and transparent investigation into Primodos risks, including whether red tape or legal procedures hindered objectivity? Were factors like the Official Secrets Act, *"Commercial Confidence"*, and interpurtations of the 1968 Medicines Act, implemented in 1971 at issue? Even Dr Iman said the Committee for Drug Safety would have been seen as transparent, but following 1971 it became called the Committee for Medicines Safety; *and "Its workings became opaque once the Medicines Act became effective in 1971"* [9, p27]. Although Dr Gall's efforts suggest it was less than transparent from 1967 onward.

Jason Farrell's Sky documentary implies prior to 1971 drug regulators in the UK may have been ineffective or worse [7]. It is difficult to say whether any Senior Medical Officer would have been placed in an impossible situation of operating in an even handed way, given the context and proximity of large drug corporations vested interests. However this is no reason to excuse either the procedures or the decisions made and these areas today require serious revisiting, to ensure history doesn't repeat or rhyme in the future; plus in addition to deal with any potential injustices previously over looked, or not adequately acknowledged.

Such insights are deeply troubling when considering this was supposedly the safety net to protect the public from vested interests, of large powerful drug corporations

profitering at the expence of human safety. Not least as
the issue by implication goes far wider than only one single
drug alone. It highlights transferable concerns of erroneous
assumed peremters of safety during pregnancy post
1962 regarding *Thalidomide*, as the Committie on Safety
of Drugs (C.S.D.) arose from the debacle around 1964 [9, pXII]. None of this challenged the flawed and erroneous
assertions of only a 9 week sensitve time window in early
pregnancy for *Thalidomide*, and has contributed to some
of the unresolved issues that have lingered to the present
day. This again points to a flawed approach of considering
stastitcal data without adequate attention to what the
statistics are showing in relation to what. As is often
referred to in the infamous saying on statistics.

It appears very similar assumptions of early pregnancy
sensitivity perameters were universally applied to all
other medications taken during pregnancy. In the case of
Primodos only a 6 week window appears to have been the
foundation for many of the assumptions of possible harm.
Yet what specific testing was conducted to underpin such
assertions remains unclear. Dr Inman stated, many of the
cases highlighted in Dr Gall's work and even his own were
too late to have caused spina bifida from HPT exposures if
HPT had been a terratogen. It appears the drug companies
and bio-symbiotic areas of esablishment, as in the case
of *Thalidomide,* were again establishing prejudicial pre-
determining criteria.

It maybe the case, a given drug has a limited narrow
time window for causing potential harm, but making
such assuptions as a starting point is not objective or
constructive. Thus the real potential for error and the
extent, is overlooking unknown and unconsidered levels of
hazard. In turn this assumes reduced assocaited levels of

risk as it has become intrinsically part of such assumptions.

Take even only a handful of seconds to glance at an atlas of feotal development, for example by Marjorie England [10]. It graphically reveals explicit undeniable photographic evidence that continuous foetal developement goes way beyond only 6 or 9 weeks. In the pre-embroyonic period, commencing day one when sperm and egg cell fuse together, a zygote cluster of cells forms. After around days 20 to 22, the embryonic period commences continuing upto c.8 to 9 weeks. Thereafter for the rest of pregnancy feotal development follows. Between weeks 9 (days 63) through to at least weeks 26 (days 182) continual physical developmental changes occur [10].

Highly significant, but out of sight, is ongoing brain formation. During weeks c.27 to 40 (days upto c.280) things may become more nuanced as to whether a fetous is developing in an unreturnable way or whether the feotus is mearly growing? That is whether missed growth might be able to be achieved more gradually, or caught up later, or not? But even here it maybe the case a drug may have the potential to degrade and damage what has already developed. It is highly doubtful foetal brain development post weeks 27 to full term of pregnancy is entirely understood, and therefore caution is without question the wiser and safer option, i.e. avoid all drug consumption throughout all of pregnancy, in a mysterious way.

Today the drug regulators M.H.R.A. says Dr Gall's evidence methodology had flaws; but if this was believed in 1967, then why did they eight years later, in 1975, put warning labels in red ink on the packets? During these years Dr Gall fought UK authorities to remove the drug, and for more funding to study and test safety concerns further. However Dr Gall got neither, and Primodos

continued to be used on pregant women. Archives in
the UK show a correpondence by Dr Inman containing
disparaging remarks concerning Dr Gall who first warned
of risks from Primodos concerning spinal damage, but in
complete contraditction acknolgedged the eight year gap
for action was inexcusable. Documentation held in archives
in Berlin implies safety testing evidence for Primodos may
have been destroyed [6]. This is yet another disturbing
similarity with *Thalidomide*, where records and test results
mysteriously likewise went missing from around 1962 to
1968 leading up to legal action [11, p46-p47, p188-p190] [12, p41].

In 1982 people alleging Primodos had caused
malformations dropped legal action as they were advised
they would be unlikely to win. Again as in the case of
Thalidomide, it was made out there was no point to legal
action, because it would probably cost the plantifs more
than the drug companies [7]. However Schering (now owned
by Bayer) were a lot less certain, if not more nervous than
they may have publicaly appeared. Schering had been
warned by their legal advisors in the UK they would be
found in breach of duty [7]. Yet strangley this was never
comunicated to the families who aledged harms were
caused by Primodos.

Schering in South Korea knew Primodos was being
used as an abortive drug, i.e. a drug to terminate
pregnancy, yet at the same time they knew women in the
UK were being given the drug to test for new life [7]. This
is very much like *Thalidomide,* where tests had shown
some abiltiy for *Thalidomide* to kill cancer cells [13], yet
Grünenthal continued to claim *Thalidomide* to be *"Atoxic"*
and "completely safe" to the unborn [11, p209-p210]; but clearly
developing human life is in essence the formation of new
cells that could easily be killed.

Knowing the wildly contradictory uses of Primodos type medications makes it hard to believe the drug might not be potentially very harmful if used in pregnancy. Today therefore it is imperative new testing is conducted to establish the levels of risk and the types of harm that may have occurred for mothers who took Primodos and similar compouds during pregnancy.

The most recent development in the struggle for families aledging Primodos harm on developing human embryo's had another set back for transparency in November 2017. A long awaited report by a working group set up by the Comission on Human Medicines (CHM), on an overview of reconsidering perevious evidence fell a long way below what had been hoped for [14]. Concern had been growing for a while regarding the terms of reference the report would take [15]. The families expressing concern over the safety of Promodos had believed new evidence would be considered. Although much evidence dated back decades, and had been only recently been uncovered as it had been withheld from public attention [7].

The publically presented report of 15th November 2017 has widely been described in the media and from all sides of parliment as a complete white wash, due to how it had critcal parts of the doumment cut out from an edition compliled only a month earlier [14]. Former Health Minister Anna Soubry told the house of commons she smelled somthing like a very big rat, raising conerns of cover up. Rt Hon M.P. Anna Soubry compared it to a comtinated blood scandle that calimed 2400 lives [16].

The November 2017 CHM Primodos report provided a sence of some uncanny echos to the Sir Alan Marre *Thalidomide* report in 1978. It chose not to acknoledge highly regarded clinitians and scienctists that provided a quite different explaintion of *Thalidomide* harms, and also extended the range and extent of harm the durg caused. Evidence pointing to harms caused by a link to antiangiogenisis and damage to the developing vasular system, as a precursor as infact is the case, was ignored in favour of the misguided nueral crest theory/ hyposisis that convientely reduced the financial cost to the liablity holders.

> ## "Being open to finding answers to questions not yet asked can provide insights and solutions to things not yet contemplated, realised or even considered"
>
> **Paul 1995**

Dr Neil Vargesson, the scientist who demonstrated *Thalidomdie* harms were and are caused by antiangiogenesis, has also made some studies with Primodos on zebra fish (particularly suited to representing aspects of human pregnancy). Initial findings have produced deeply disturbing affects, when considering potental risks to safety if consumed during pregnancy [7]. As in *Thalidomdie*, the above Primodos test results indicate harms occur in relation to timeline embryogenesis, i.e. different development aspects contained within relevant time windows are negatively affected.

There are yet futher drugs with lingering concerns regarding consumption during pregnancy, and they also need further testing to upgrade medical and scientific underdstanding. Dr Neil Vargesson at Aberdeen University

Medical Science Department is perhaps already becoming a defacto goto National testing centre for embryo and feotal drug safety. It would offer potential for wider indpendent national terratogen testing. The benefit would be to establish objective appreciation for all levels of potential risks from chemcial compounds to cause harm on the unborn, at any and every stage of prebirth formation, development, and growth. This was effectively what was being called for by *Thalidomide* families in the 1960's, but declined and ignored ever since.

It would be good to think this at last offers the start of more open and transparent testing in relation to drugs terrragenic risks, despite being more than five decades

A word to the wise
(Photography support: Barn Owl Centre,
Gloucestershire GL2 5LE)

overdue. It is vital all drug and medical health testing is entirely objective and totally free from all influence from any vested interests, including that of arms length through settlement bodies/ trusts.

Another drug that would benefit from greater understanding is the drug Debendox, *Bendiectin* in the US, and may have had other trade names? This was another drug given to pregnant women for morning sickness. During the drug's history it has gone from a three compound to a two compound drug, and consequently the different formulae may alter on how it has interacted during gestation of developing new life. Debendox was a drug some women took during pregancy in the 1960's, 1970's, and perhaps later? In some instances women who took Debendox during pregnancy gave birth to a baby with malformations and or health issues. Where this happened it has been alleged there was a connection between the malformations/ health issues and the Debondox/ *Bendiectin* taken.

An amazing person I know whose mother who took Debendox during pregancy, has noted adverse physical challenges she faces are consistent with impacts in the relevant feotal development time window while Debendox was being consumed. People who alleged Debendox caused damage to the unborn continue to suggest there is real potential to learn more. They advocate new objective and indpendent science, using well thought out innovative questions in new and fresh ways too help to reconsider the issues they claim remain unacknowledged and unaddressed.

Debendox has a long history and an in-depth account is beyond the scope for this book. The drug was manufactured by Merrell, part of a number of companies that has subsequently merged and morphed over the years. Debendox/ *Bendectin* began with in the US in the mid to late 1950's, around the time when the company tried to gain a liecence for *Thalidomdie*, combined with the unethical 'Investigational Program/ marketing trials'. In addtion around this time Merrell had another drug with serious side effect issues, code named Mer 29 that resulted in considerable reporation for people harmed [17].

One would like to think large pharmaceutical companies of contempary times do not operate with such dubious practice? It would be easy to assume such issues would no longer be relevant today, with greater health and safety protocol. In some respects this maybe the case, but all the more reason for reconsideration of potential harm caused by former drugs taken in pregnancy. A review is now required of all old legacy drugs from before and since 1971 using a broader range of drug safety questions, posed in more rounded ways. Such a process may even point to new and alternative safe uses with gains for humanity?

"When you are a student people are judged by how well you answer questions, but in life you're judged by how good your questions are" [18]

Dr Robert Langer

(Institute Professor, Massachusetts Institute of Technology)

The key is to search and find innovative ways of asking old questions, and to develop and facilitate new questions not yet asked. A wider pool of different specialists to ask new questions, including some not presently or specifically associated with drug safety, may enable new lines of enquiry and approaches. Organic ways of thinking tends to generate new creative potential for asking old questions in new ways, and questions not yet asked, or being considered in the right ways.

Epilim/ *Sodium Valporate*, is a drug used to control epileptic seizures, bipolar disorders and migraine. Allegations of miss use over decades since the 1970's of have resurfaced in 2017, as the drug carries c.10% risk of physical abnormalities and 40% risk of autism, low IQ and learning impairments [19]. For the individual developing baby affects and harms placed on them are 100%, with direct and indirect consequences that last a life time; if not perhaps reduce the lifetime also.

Epilim/*Sodium Valporate* is a drug used to help prevent epilepsy, and this can even be potentially lifesaving. Nonetheless the issue is alleged that inadequate information was provided to women who were or could be pregnant, together with a general lack of transparency, and poor treatment received by survivors who were harmed [19] [20] [21].

For all drugs where concern continues relating to potential harm from use during pregnancy, there appear to be the similar disturbing themes of; not divulging information, denial, distortion and distraction. In the case of *Sodium Valporate* highly disturbing minutes from the 18th July 1973 sub-committee on Committee on Safety of Medicines have been unearthed. They point to worse than neglect, as the suggestion was safety warnings could be buried in small print, where women who were or might be pregnant would not find them, and not to place warnings on the outer packaging [19] [20] [21].

It seems as though the authorities responsible for protecting the public, have for years acted in step, with the big drug companies' errors of judgement on safety during pregnancy. A familiar pattern of failings within the authorities has left scenarios of risk and hazard being exposed to the public they were supposedly protecting. Strong indicators point to gross intrinsic cultural failures and an appalling paternalistic approach in terms of transparency, in relation to drug safety question marks since the 1950's.

Women who were or could be pregnant and their unborn offspring appear to have been viewed and treated with contempt. Yet the reality check is; it's the mothers of babies that are harmed who carry both the hurt and many other burdens, while the drug companies are left to take pleasure in enhanced profits, and ministers wallow in their ego of a chauffeur driven ride.

The aerospace industry is often held up as the gold standard for other industries to emulate in terms of safety. One of the most significant factors is how all companies and participants are obliged to share information to prevent accidents and promote safe flying.

Regulators, governments, professional bodies and other institutions can suffer amnesia, as day to day cultural knowledge does not always get passed on to a new generation of people. Sometimes this can be stage managed and only present a victor's narrative. For decades there has been a considerable amnesia in the *Thalidomide* drug companies; an approach that has left a legacy of failure to address the past, and thereby leaves open potential for future error. For example use of drugs in developing countries, and or for different purposes and issues but retaining overlapping concerns. This can even be with derivatives or analogues of a drug as in the case of *Thalidomide*. Such drugs can be known by different names, and may have little direct reference to the ancestral/ family of drugs.

Taking into account a drug's potential to harm or impair a developing baby at any stage of gestation will require looking at all processes. This includes education/ training that at present seems to professionally indoctrinate people to stop thinking in an unhindered and open way. Challenging perspectives, will require breaking free from all straight jacketed modus operandi driven by assumptions of what could not be; for example 6, or 9 week timescale limitations in pregnancy. A Radio 4 programme: *Saving Science from the Scientists* by Alok Jha [22] touched on some surrounding issues of objectivity, revealing sometimes the science needs checking independently.

Another BBC Radio 4 programme, Analysis, focused on organisational amnesia, and how culturally things become lost over generations of employee contributors. With the length of employment contracts decreasing continuity results, something that increases organisational/ institutional amnesia [23]. One interesting suggestion was assigning organisational memory tasks or roles to individuals in an integrated way to pass on memories to the next generation. Such approaches may be valuable for drug regulatory bodies and the NHS on medical issues more widely.

Going forward both public and medical professions require open transparent objective accounts of all past drugs mentioned above and perhaps others, to assess hazards and risks. This is to ensure drugs are not inadvertently used in error, particularly where the use is changed. Such action would also help to provide trust and confidence in official safety advice in the future more generally. Challenging and combating amnesia needs to be extended to all settlement organisations for drugs and other health issues, along with independent oversight to facilitate learning and sharing of knowledge.

Kiazen [24]

(Japanese for Continual improvement)

21

C. S. R. – Having Cake and Eating It?

Corporate Social Responsibility (C.S.R.) is a wide umbrella term referring to the underlying tenants of ethical business and trading. It concerns implementing good practice in; social, ethical, health and safety/ wellbeing, plus environmental conduct at all stages, and in all areas of business. This includes customers/ clients, employees and contractors. These factors become intrinsic core business/ organisational objectives to develop and establish a brand and name for high standards. In turn this develops the market for an ethical business environment, and levers power to drive up standards across an entire sector or industry.

Mad as a hatter's tea party?

"All management is risk management" [1]
Douglas Barlow (1907-1998)

There are many good examples of sound medical practice and responsible pharmaceutical operations in research, sales and prescribing. Good practice exists where remedial and mitigating action is swiftly and robustly put in place when things don't always go to plan. At the right levels at times of human need pharmaceutical drugs are commendable, even noble for humanity. It is imperative pressure also comes from within the industry to ensure all mistakes and wayward legacies are corrected. Corporations and organisations upholding good practice do not need to be silent apologists, for poor standards or unjustifiable operators. Above all C.S.R. must be more, than simply a cost of doing business.

Any drugs currently or formerly taken in pregnancy where question marks or concerns still linger, no matter how small, require the provision of independent and transparent research to answer all residual concerns. Where the answers arrived at reveal new information, then action and proactive steps to resolve and counter any and all revealed errors is essential. This includes the explicit communication of what the errors were and how their presentation has been misleading.

The BMJ has highlighted concerns with poor and over prescribing of drugs, including antipsychotic medication for people in vulnerable groups. This has included those with autism and learning difficulties [2], where the drugs purpose could be seen as being used as primarily a form of patient control.

Dr Fiona Godlee as BMJ chief editor has called for more transparent independently operated drug trials, compared to the present situation led by an industry bias funded approach. More independence would enable clinicians to make better informed decisions [3]. It is remarkable to think this was effectively the same issue put to the Minister for Health in 1962 by the families of people born with malformations due to *Thalidomide* exposure during pregnancy.

"So much of what we call management consists in making it difficult for people to work" [4]

Peter Drucker

Since the Mid Staff's inquiry into poor health care and high mortality rates at Stafford Hospital, an independent report was made in 2015 regarding treatment of Whistle-Blowers within the NHS. The 'Freedom to Speak Up' report commissioned by the government was said to address concerns of a culture obstructing transparency and openness on serious health care issues. The report was based on evidence from 600 individuals and 43 organisations across the country. It included disconcerting accounts from doctors, nurses and healthcare professionals claiming their lives' and careers had been left badly damaged after trying to raise legitimate concerns about patient safety. A spectrum of bullying and punitive measures such as job black listing and financial undoing are claimed by people who say they spoke up for transparency. It leaves an impression that the Health Trusts reputations and financial interests may have been a higher priority than transparency into patient care. Whistle blowers in health care and medicine sectors need legal immunity and protection [5].

"Efficiency is doing the right things, Effectiveness is doing things right" [6]

Peter Ducker

Bad practice and a lack of transparency concerning *Thalidomide* continues to linger over five decades on. This includes how propaganda and misinformation on the extent and range of unacknowledged harms caused by the drug, managed to hoodwink many professionals and the public since the 1960's. It is likely the same fear of threats to career and employment, were significant factors in silencing many in the medical and associated professions on *Thalidomide* issues over the decades. In the 1970's Dr Poswillo valiantly fought for the recognition of unilateral injuries and myriad of other harm he had observed in his and other clinical studies [7] [8, p67-p73]. Dr Poswillo and others believed the onus needed to be on the drug companies, to prove a malformation or complication did not result from *Thalidomide*, rather than the other way around.

Despite being years after it was publically known *Thalidomide* could kill cancer cells [9], the contradictions promoted by *Thalidomide* drug companies continued. These were founded on the inaccurate neural crest theory/ hypothesis that bamboozled mainstream medical thinking into believing *Thalidomide* could only mysteriously harm developing cells, on a limited number of specific select days within the first 9 weeks of pregnancy.

Such an approach was and is the opposite of C.S.R. good practice. In the early 1970's Distillers Company Ltd through their Trust sought to use a divide and rule approach for the cohort of people it acknowledged and recognised as harmed by *Thalidomide*. David Mason, father of *Thalidomide* survivor Louise Mason made a brave fight during this time against the Trust and drug companies. As a result he eventually won a much better settlement deal for recognised *Thalidomide* survivors [10] [11, p314-p337]. However in 1978 there were no further such courageous challenges against the Sir Alan Marre report findings and from this point onward the drug companies imposed their version of history and medical recognition.

The Alan Marre Report in 1978 [12] was supposed to deal with two categories of people claiming to be *Thalidomide* survivors. There was an "X" list of people the drug companies stated may have signs of *Thalidomide* harms (a gross underestimate). Plus the "Y" list (probably only the tip of the iceberg), a group of people who claimed to have been harmed by *Thalidomide* but did not conform to type re; the official line based on bias recognition criteria. The *Thalidomide* Trust UK provided arms length manoeuvring for the *Thalidomide* drug companies'/ liability holders and bio-symbiotic areas of the establishment. Since the concept of the settlement Trust, it provided the facility to divide and rule, pitching one *Thalidomide* survivor, against another.

People alleging *Thalidomide* harms were channelled through a single gateway that was bias towards the position of Distillers Company Ltd, via referral a legal solicitor Kimber Bull & Co. For review leading up to the Alan Marre report 1978 there was one medic who over saw proceedings; Professor Richard Smithells of Leeds University. He was clearly sided towards the *Thalidomide* drug companies' predispositions, and operated to their self serving list of recognition characteristics.

These recognition characteristics drastically underestimated the level and extent of harms the drug could cause. They were flawed and errant but promoted

by the drug companies through their arms length 3rd
party settlement organisation and trusts. Their research
determined who joined the "X" list, and who would be left
out in the "Y" list. The drug companies wanted to deny new
recognitions, continuing to claim only limited impairments
or malformations existed, and these could only be present
in tandem with phocomelia (no or high levels of reductions
in arms or, and legs). It created a requirement to conform
to type; a very narrow sub set of interpretation, limited
to only recognising bilateral malformations. Yet plenty
of evidence for years had suggested a great deal more
harms and damage had occurred, including unilateral
harms that had gone unrecognised [13, p199-p200]. Dr Poswillo
believed there were potentially many different atypical
malformations and harms due to *Thalidomide* that had not
been satisfactorily explained [7] [8, p67-p73].

Ironically the then medical officer for TTUK at the time,
Dr Philip Quibell produced an unpublished manuscript
concluding a huge number of people were affected by
Thalidomide, but had not been recognised due to flawed
assessments [13, p199-p200]. No surprise this report did not
get published. What happened to Dr Philip Quibell I don't
know, but suspect he was either reined in, or let go at some
convenient juncture soon after, for not being 100% on
message.

Distinguished developmental biologist Professor Lewis
Wolpert submitted another unpublished document for the
TTUK, describing the neural crest theory/ hypothesis as;
*"very weak foundation… (which)…is contrary to all known
embryological studies"*. Wolpert dismissed neural crest
theory/ hypothesis as *"most unlikely"*, suggesting *"damage
to the vascular system of the early limb bud" as a much
more likely causation"* [13, p199-p200]. It turns out that Wolpert,

Jurrand and others had been right all along. Thus clearly Dr Poswillo et.al had very good reasons to be sceptical of the drug companies and governmental self serving interest of protecting their narrative. This assumed only a limited 9 week sensitive period that mysteriously contradicted known biological observations in general and strangely could not be explained, but nonetheless was remarkably financial convenient.

During David Mason's campaign against the settlement body *Thalidomide* Trust UK of the early 1970's [10] [11, p314-p337], the UK public perhaps first became introduced to the concept of Corporate Social Responsibility (C.S.R.). Sarah Broad a Distillers share holder became Chair of a sub group committee that fought to improve an appalling low settlement offer from Distillers Company Ltd [10] [11]. What Sarah Broad and others would not have known, was how many other people had never been recognised or accounted for and the wide range of unrecognised harms the drug had caused. Nonetheless Sarah Broad, M.P. Jack Ashley, David Mason, journalist Harold Evans, and a few other people significantly helped more of the severely harmed *Thalidomide* survivors to get a much better deal, and gained further help from the UK Government [10] [11, p314-p337].

However ground breaking C.S.R. regrettably had some catches imposed by Distillers Company Ltd and bio-symbiotic domains of government. In the small print of the deal for better settlements for the recognised *Thalidomide* survivors, a new discrimination was established in the form of the "X" and "Y" lists that ignored people they chose to disregard in the first place [8] [12] [13, p199-p200].

Even the extended "Y" list back in 1978 would have been nowhere near the total number of people harmed by

Thalidomide; in part as many who had been harmed likely would not even have been aware the drug was responsible for a wide range of other ailments and conditions.

Today all *Thalidomide* Settlement bodies and sub/ inter-organisations require independent over sight, plus some overhauling to present wider transparency. This is essential to provide a clear explanation of all *Thalidomide* harms before birth, and how they can impact on all stages of pregnancy. As the UK government since the early 1970's and again under Gordon Browns premiership has contributed £Millions of public money [11, p332-p336], it is not only right, it is essential settlement bodies are subject to absolute public transparency and accountability.

All untold historical accounts and information needs to be presented front and centre on all websites plus supporting information, as well as off line. It is vital not the slightest smallest amount of mealy mouth sidestepping wiggle room is allowed to even hint at propping up any slightest falsehood or sham interpretations. Where inaccurate information has been put out, the correct updated information must be prominently displayed on into the future for all in both the medical profession and the public to see; including NHS and related websites/ BBC, medical text books etc.

At present transparency continues to remain opaque, as much by how information has quietly disappeared or simply being silently omitted. As a result the legacy of a disturbing sanitized set of impressions, and sound bites continues to imply drastic misconceived limitations; on both timescales in pregnancy for harm to occur and the types, range and extent of harm *Thalidomide* can and has caused but not previously acknowledged.

This is important firstly for justice for people impacted

in previous episodes, and secondly as the drug or analogues could cause harm in the future, and such harms would not be even detected or related to consumption of the drug. The consultant in child growth I saw in my childhood was one of a handful of specialist doctors who with the backdrop of then recent history, and his observations of my x-rays and biometrics appreciated *Thalidomide* negatively impacted me way beyond and eccentric allocation of days within the first 9 weeks of pregnancy. Nonetheless he was powerless against the might of the drug companies and government power that had a hold over the medical profession. See chapter 3 Growing Concerns.

Retrospective observations were the starting point for determining what if any limits there were for *Thalidomide* to harm developing babies. Based on established interpretations only babies with none existent or very significantly reduced limbs would be deemed to have been harmed by the drug, leaving a huge vacuum of awareness amongst the medical profession; such that future harms would not even be identified.

For example a child presents with a heart complication form birth or perhaps not noticed until aged 7 years old. Who then would relate to *Thalidomide* or an analogue taken by the child's mother during around weeks 13 to 14 of her pregnancy? The same would apply for lung impairment during this time, or brain impairment caused between weeks 19 to 24, or a malfunctioning spleen resulting from exposure at weeks 11 to 21, or hearing loss from exposure during week 15. Potentially there could be an infinite myriad of health complications/ syndromes/ metal impairments, yet in a person with both arms and legs at full proportions plus feet and hands as to be expected.

Diageo the drinks and beverage corporate superpower inherited *Thalidomide* legacy liabilities derived from ancestral links to Distillers Company Ltd. In many ways Diageo has quite a good C.S.R. record, and even beyond what might be expected; for example being prepared to take a loss in sales and profits to challenge discrimination of gay people in Canada's St Patricks Day activities [14]. Such commendable action of putting social concerns above profit is a good sign. However an array of unrecognised different *Thalidomide* harms, also now needs to be acknowledged worldwide. Diageo operating with good C.S.R. needs to make a public stand against Grünenthal for these ends. Besides being uplifting, if Diageo demonstrated the best C.S.R. practice they would most likely bring the public on side with them by doing the right thing; even if it meant crossing lines previously agreed with Grünenthal and UK or German Governments that have previously hindered transparency.

Additional requirements continue for governmental C.S.R., to ensure regulations along with statutory obligations/ duties are upheld and reviewed. Long overdue greater supervision concerning the vacuum of oversight is required for settlement bodies/ trusts to protect the public and professions. Transparency and validity of all assertions made by, or passed on from settlement organisations/ entities need independent oversight and vetting. It is also essential such oversight has mechanisms for acting if and when members of the public become concerned something(s) is/are a miss.

Narratives that are partly inaccurate are the most difficult falsehoods to notice as they wear the clothes of rectitude, appearing to be correct throughout. Action today needs to challenge and over turn all expediency effects where other third parties are or have been influenced, into taking or promoting (however unwittingly/ subliminally) a position to favour an errant or even partially false narrative of a settlement entity. In the case of *Thalidomide* Trust their expediency ultimately has historically covered the backs of the wayward drug companies and compliant bio-symbiotic areas of the establishment. Such underlying addenda's can easily become projected onto all in their ambit, for example; the media and or other parties supported or informed by settlement bodies as they hold the power role over others.

An overriding influential sway can effortlessly occur from a subtle steer through the power of financial incentive. This may be direct, or even through more subtle indirect ways. Up to now the self appointed authority status of *Thalidomide* settlement bodies have dominated all other perspectives, promoting bogus stances, supported by a position of impregnable power over others with more enlightened perspectives. The status quo needs to be over turned and the full recognition criteria made transparently public now, not in another 50 years time.

Thalidomide Trust UK was originally established by Distillers Company Ltd, sided with Grünenthal and the other *Thalidomide* drug companies. In unison a watertight on message loop excluded many people from recognition of *Thalidomide* harms, to enable limiting numbers of people they had to acknowledge as *Thalidomide* harmed, but legally denied anyway. Inaction by the *Thalidomide* Trust UK since their conception around 1969 resulted in the early C.S.R. campaign by Sarah Broad's, and David Mason in the early 1970's mentioned above [10] [11, p333].

Distillers Company Ltd and partners in wrong doing Grünenthal continued to make denials on time frames for harm. UK and German Government failings ensured the *Thalidomide* drug companies were not held to full account before, during or after the drugs "withdrawal" from the wholesaler c.1962. This back drop enabled the *Thalidomide* drug companies in unanimity to establish a consistent, (but false) on message approach, and dominate dissenting voices of scientists, clinicians and unacknowledged *Thalidomide* survivors. The residual was propagated through settlement trusts/ organisations to fob off awkward questions, and ring fenced financial losses to only limited amounts. It also meant cohorts of people before and after 1962 have been exposed to *Thalidomide* after 9 weeks in pregnancy, assured it was completely safe in later pregnancy; my mother was one such example in early 1966. Yet the harms it caused have still not been recognised or acknowledged thus far, necessitating *"16 Weeks and Everything After..."©* to bypass all the official road blocks to transparency established and facilitated by the context of settlement bodies, along with bio-symbiotic areas of the establishment.

Settlement Trusts/ bodies directly or indirectly however inertly have facilitated other channels to propagate their misinformation, including; influencing support/ self help groups, charitable organisations, medical and science channels. In turn this indirectly facilitates the unwitting mainstream media to act like a Trojan and vicariously propagate their denial, distortion and distraction.

Within some corners of medical institutions there also needs to be some genuine reflection, in particular concerning revaluation of whistle blowing policy and protocol for wider scrutiny. It is clear some medical voices did speak up for the evidence of wider harms of *Thalidomide*, but were repeatedly overrun and subjugated.

The *Thalidomide* drug companies/ liability holders in effect planted a mole right at the heart of power. As a result the medical profession more widely were duped, and filed rank for the next 50 years, despite a handful of more enlightened people attempting to shine daylight on the real issues.

In the case of *Thalidomide,* the power base has opportunely ensured all accountable were able to dodge much of their full moral responsibilities and obligations.

In some developing countries *Thalidomide* has found new uses. In itself this may not be an entirely bad thing, where the drug relieves suffering and doesn't produce unwanted side effects. However it is depressing to learn *Thalidomide* use has indirectly resulted in causing harm on unborn babies with recognised affects. Brazil is one such country [15], but most likely nobody has any idea how many people may have been harmed beyond the first trimester, i.e. after weeks 12; if even accurate numbers are really known for the first trimester?

Other similar types of disturbing scenarios occur where analogues of *Thalidomide* are used but remain even less considered in terms of risks to harm to the unborn, and much less communicated to either medic or patient. *Thalidomide* or analogues is available in 48 countries, and may be given for medical conditions such as Crohn's disease, or neurodermatitis skin conditions and other reasons [16].

In how many of the 48 countries *Thalidomide* was sold before the 1962 "withdrawal" from the wholesale market began, I don't know. It would not be a surprise to discover it was mostly about the same approximately 48 *Thalidomide* was originally sold in the 1960's. Again highlighting the significance to the drug companies of ensuring the drug was not banned, but instead only underwent a "withdrawal" from the wholesale market; enabling a quiet return to the market for redirected purposes but with the prospect of not that many questions being asked.

It highlights how an ongoing opaque picture has left a real knowledge vacuum, silently potentially placing the risk of hazard onto professionals and patients, without either even knowing. Only as recently as 2016 and 2017 in Europe three women resulted to terminations after taking analogues of *Thalidomide* while pregnant, but it seems were not warned of the dangers of *Thalidomide* type drugs [16]. Denmark, the Netherlands, Spain (ironic given Spain has never even fully acknowledged people more extremely harmed by *Thalidomide*), and Sweden appears to have prescribed the drug without giving adequate warnings for even the officially recognised risks [16], let alone those after the first trimester that have always existed but are still not recognised or acknowledged.

Wider concerns extend to conditions surrounding *Thalidomide* and analogues, where regulatory control may be getting slackened in the US, as a way of lowering drug costs. It is reported Scott Gottlieb advised US Congress REMS, an evaluation process, should be relaxed, whereas at the moment *Thalidomide* can be prescribed but only when birth control and the risks of pregnancy are explained [16]. Again how ironic given the world leading heroic stand by Dr Kelsey at the F.D.A in the 1960's against the use of *Thalidomide,* until it could be proven to be safe throughout all of pregnancy.

It is never going to be either good practice or safe to loosen any regulatory control of *Thalidomide* and its analogues. If anything what is needed is a stepping up, not a slackening off. If a medical professional picks up a text book almost regardless of which country they are in, the chances are the impression they will be left with is after 9 weeks, (or maybe in some rare but more recent publications 12 weeks of pregnancy). The real risk is that it would therefore be assumed *Thalidomide* is safe to use after such time lines. BUT **THIS IS WRONG AND ALWAYS HAS BEEN WRONG – THERE NEVER WAS OR IS A SAFE TIME TO CONSUME *THALIDOMIDE* (OR ANALOGUES) DURING PREGNANCY – IN ANY WEEKS ZERO ALL THE WAY THROUGH TO FULL TERM.**

The real risks today are not only the inherent risks of teratogens, but perhaps as significantly, how young women today are in general no longer aware what the *Thalidomide* nightmare was all about. These factors are exacerbated so long as time limits remain wayward. A combination of ignorance by both medic and mother has the potential, to expose her developing baby to harms and impairments for life by *Thalidomide* (or analogues) not even officially acknowledged or in medical text books.

Research and assessment has in the past been misdirected to asking the wrong questions, like sending a dog to bark up the wrong tree. Looking in the incorrect places distracted from ever looking in the right places, thus proliferating and perpetuating confusion with unanswerable quandaries. In turn this neatly fed back, into the loop of the established residual myth and narrative of mysterious and unknowable accounts, facilitating a complete impasse. Thus the *Thalidomide* misinformation and propaganda has misadvised the medical professions and public for over 50 years; backed up by, and through, a self (righteous) appointed channel and oracle of authority.

There have been many wrong doers and dodgers of

justice, in the long silent lingering *Thalidomide* nightmare and none more so than Grüthenthal the German drug company that first brought the deplorable drug *Thalidomide*, to the market in the late 1950's. In September 2012 Grünenthal by way of Harold Stock, the C.E.O. at the time, made their shameful dismal official *"apology"* statement for the *Thalidomide* disaster; but this fell far below the minimum standard of a real apology, sought by both survivors and society. Even this came only weeks after Australian lawyers fighting a case for *Thalidomide* survivor Lynette Rowe, had finally obtained release of German Court Documents from the 1970 case [17] [18].

Since the worse than pathetic 2012 *"apology"* by Grünenthal, further airbrushing on Grünenthal website has removed direct information of *Thalidomide,* reduced to a link to a separate website that does not acknowledge anything new. Yet thousands of babies did not survive due to the drug, and thousands more were harmed as a result,

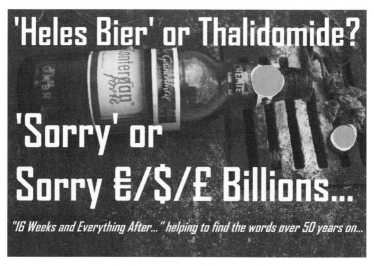

Real sincerity is still required

and thousands more again would have been harmed but remain unaccounted for.

By 2017 other legacy/ settlement organisations websites have received various airbrushing plus have become a great deal trendier, yet many issues are left unresolved. At the time of writing the current TTUK website has made a reference to a time line they recognised as *Thalidomide* harmed being only as late as 1965, yet is buried in a section for application to be a beneficiary. On the main part of the website is an implied a 1965 timeline, by now acknowledging ages of people are between 52 and 58 in 2017. However this fails to acknowledge timelines undoubtedly went beyond 1965, as my exposure to *Thalidomide* was into 1966, albeit early in the year, and I find it hard to believe I was the last.

My suspicion is *Thalidomide* most probably only really finally started to fade out completely, when legal proceedings began against the drug company taking place in 1968; after a 6 year vacuum where unknown amounts had been used in later pregnancy. By then with wider events of the 1960's the public were becoming less naive, and *Thalidomide* had also lost its lustre from doctors' perspectives; especially with the advent of the Medicines Act where they for the first time had had to write down medication given and this meant they could face legal action;. Yet even after 1968 it is likely some further cases would have occurred, not least as affects beyond 9 weeks in pregnancy were being denied by 'experts' then as they are now.

Trendy websites don't per se deal with legacies of 5 decades, of incomplete information on timelines of harm in pregnancy. Nor have they confronted or openly and transparently explained what constitutes *Thalidomide* harm

All mothers want justice for **all** drugs that harmed babies during pregnancy

either, and that the real full account is contrary to what TTUK have projected for the last 50 years. If anything in some respects the direction of travel is slightly backwards, as even the previously limited information formerly made available to the public has also been sidelined. Now it is even clubbier, as only those people they have allowed to be registered by their recognition procedures can gain access, assuming anything significant remains? As TTUK is in part financed with public money, more needs to be accessible directly by the public, and open to meaningful challenges where error is found or suspected.

The weapon of silence is all the more powerful the longer time goes on, facilitating further sanitization by quietly leaving out information. As memories and ties to the 1960's *Thalidomide* scandal recede further, real jeopardy exists many of its lessons will be lost before they have even been learnt. The seeds of future tragedies have already been sown, potentially resulting in babies being harmed in the future and no one will even necessarily know or realise harm in other time windows has occurred. Where harm does occur it would not be realised it was the consequence of *Thalidomide/* analogues, because the residual recognition criteria is and always has been insidiously flawed.

The No Limits documentary involving some *Thalidomide* survivors highlighted how the Grüthenthal Company profited from the disaster resulting today in huge wealth. Lawyer Michael Magazanik commented; the Wirtz family has a personal fortune variously estimated between €2 to 3 Billion [17] [18].

Globally society has been waiting for over 50 years, for *Thalidomide* drug companies together with brand Germany, and brand UK to demonstrate sincere and commensurate societal contrition from stakeholders responsible. In the UK errors began under the watch of Minister for Health Enoch Powell [11, p314-p318]. Following initial ineptness there was a lack of rigor to publically investigate, ascertain, and scrutinize all that had gone wrong, and then to put on public record [19, p183-p191]. The seeds of involvement with the inner loop of *Thalidomide* drug companies persisted, given space and legitimacy by reprehensible inaction from governments in the UK and Germany.

Corporate Social Responsibility continues to have a way to go for both *Thalidomide* drug companies plus UK and German governments. Going forward it provides opportunities to demonstrate proactive precedent for other drugs that may also require satisfactory resolutions, as well establishing good practice in UK and German collaboration. All the information of the *Thalidomide* trials from 1965 through to 1968, as well as the main trial from 1968 to 1970 in archives stores need to be digitalized and put online. Something one assumes would be no problem on harnessing German efficiency.

Part or full German government management could potentially mortgage the future of Grünenthal for wider societal good. It would also be an appropriate moment to create joint funded drug testing facilities, especially for safety during pregnancy but also more widely as an example of good mutual post Brexit co-operation. The UK government needs to ensure public bodies are legally liable for inaction and or obstruction of safety obligations, and the public have the facility to take action. It would be timely as there have been calls in relation to the Hillsborough tragedy for extending legal safeguards and comeback, where public bodies cover up, withhold information, and fail to act in the public interest.

No more cake and eating it

An Anglo German pursuit of drug safety during pregnancy has the opportunity to promote the very best practice globally, and involve/ develop specialist skill sets from around the world. Such a positive legacy would provide an independent entity with one or possibly two head quarters, e.g. one in the UK one in Germany, then fielded out to relevant specialists that offered the skills required. As a starting point it requires sincere fresh reviews of all drugs from the 1950's (possibly earlier) that have continued lingering question marks, or greater concern for safety during pregnancy. UK and German governments need to see this as an opportunity not a threat, it may have multiple valuable spin offs.

Anything less than a totally satisfactory C.S.R. outcome for society in general and **all** *Thalidomide* survivors, and **all** survivors of **all** other harmful drugs consumed in pregnancy, including those not previously recognised or acknowledged would only be describable as; C.S.R. Having cake and eating it.

'Change is not made without inconvenience, even form worse to better' [20]

Richard Hooker (1554-1600)

22

The Road Ahead...

There are no claims of being a writer, and writing another book is not envisaged, hence it's probably best not to hold your breath if wondering about a sequel; *'More Adventures Post 16 Weeks...'©'*, although perhaps it is not entirely ruled out.

Researching, writing and producing *"16 Weeks and Everything After..."©* was metaphorically like a set of Russian Dolls as I was not quite certain there might not yet be even more to discover or to be worked on, and perhaps there is? Many journeys occurred and co-existed within a larger overall journey. Nonetheless at all stages negatives

Russian dolls are beautiful but 60 years of Thalidomide suppression is not

have been viewed with the intent of turning them into positives and a spur to greater creativity for future times.

Going forward will integrate some reflective time and exploring of new things, while recharging my energy. Time will tell what further options, opportunities and actions may be possible on the Distaval/*Thalidomide* trail?

In the rest of life there are other goals to go for. One of the most pressing is to somehow find a way to accomplish a modest self build house project for an environmentally friendly place to live; something that would be greatly enhanced by assisting/ co-operating with even only a handful of other people who are also shut out of both social and private housing, yet without satisfactory or realistic alternatives.

Steel is real

There has been precedent for making and building things. On a bike frame building week I made my first handmade steel bicycle frame; a road 26" wheel compact format with a front triangle in oversized Columbus Nivacrom ©/ Zona ©, plus a rear triangle of Reynolds 725 © tubes, plus front forks constructed in Reynolds 853 ©. The frame may have had some beginners luck, nonetheless the alchemy dialled in a bike offering more than the sum of its parts, and produced something of the often fabled, but much elusive *"magic carpet"* ride.

Regrettably following an unexpected spill in March 2017 the above bike frame was written off, and replacement options around a road/ gravel frame for 650b wheel size are being contemplated. Although an audio project to build a turntable for playing vinyl is also under some thought, along with other craft and creative ventures.

In ancient times building bicycles and D.I.Y. audio was less of an option, but people still needed reflective time. The Isle of Apples or Avalloc with its connection to Avalon has been suggested to date back to beyond the 12th century, and legend has it warriors would visit to regain energies expended in battle. King Arthur was said to have visited Avalon [1]. Also known as *'Arthur of the Britons'* he had strong links to Cornwall and Wales. Although some have suggested Avalon was near Caerleon and Glastonbury [2]; long before rock and contemporary music festivals were held in knee deep mud, over traffic filled bank holiday weekends.

Restorative properties of apples have already played a part over the years in my personal journey; including planting apple trees and pruning them with pull stroke arbour saws. On an old bicycle haunt there's a wonderful apple tree orchard I have on occasions stopped to

The cycle of the seasons

photograph. One of my favourite shots was taken in 2006, early in the morning on the day before harvest. Its branches were heavily labouring with its crop steeped in a deep delicious murky mist, where the chill almost freezing air clung to the ground. Back then I had no idea of all the places my personal journey would take me, but the local Avalon with only the quiet sounds of nature and the delicate floral fragrance of an impending apple gathering must have provided all the fortitude required.

"Ultimately the only currency we have is time spend it wisely and gain lasting dividends"

Paul 2015

Beyond this life I decided to donate my body for medical science to Cardiff School of Biosciences (Cardiff University) for the purpose of learning more about foetal development of weeks 16 to 20. In addition perhaps other potential medical insights from a wider perspective maybe gained? Brain development in general and dyslexia more widely perhaps and would most likely be something that would be of real interest to me if I were still around. Nonetheless my hopes are however marginally, humanity can gain in some way or ways, as a final act of turning negatives into positives.

Whether in life omens and signs really exist, who knows? Being more practically minded I tend to suspect probably not. All the same while writing *"16 Weeks and Everything After..."*© there have been a number of unpredictable coincidences. For example, commencing the project exactly 47 years to the week, and most likely even the very day the overall narrative began, plus the research was completed 50 years after on the last day of weeks 20.

Another out of the ordinary scenario occurred through an appointment to review some publishing options. It happened to be the day of the tenth anniversary of my mother's passing; hence it already felt like she was coming with me to somehow metaphorically take part in the final stages of the project.

It had been over 30 years since I last visited Peterborough. Arriving in good time before my appointment, and in no hurry I stood watching a crane start to demolish part of a wall in a building opposite. Then something occurred to me. Unsure of the real likely hood I asked a person on the platform if he was a local. *"All my life"*, he replied. So I enquired further, *"Excuse me, could you tell me what the building they are just starting to knock down was?* "Yes", he said, and continued, *"It was, the old Thorpe Road hospital"*. After a further pause he added, *"This is the last building to come down...then they'll put flats on it".* I thanked the local, and left the station to get a cab.

This had been a sort of twilight moment, as the building coming down was the final part of the hospital I was born at 49 years earlier. On returning at the end of the day, in fading daylight I waited on the platform for my train, watching the demolition crane swinging at what little remained of the hospital building. On board the train it very gradually pulled off into swirling autumnal evening mists. At the same time a full Hunter's moon hauntingly edged up from low on the horizon. What were the chances of seeing that all these years later, I reflected? One day earlier and the demolition would not have started, one day later and there would be nothing left to see. At least one in

Paul Whymark Photography ©

Powerful gravitational forces

a million, perhaps more I thought. The train began picking up speed and I contemplated how it was like a metaphor for uncovering all the findings and discoveries on my personal journey.

Two years later in 2017, I drove to a self publisher in Leicestershire to sign the contracts with the completed manuscript that is this book, *"16 Weeks and Everything After..."*©.

There have been accounts and significant nuances some had wanted entirely airbrushed out of history. This has prevented both the public and medical professionals from fully appreciating all consequences of *Thalidomide* consumed in pregnancy, and probably other drugs also. However I dared to ask different questions, and dared to ask questions differently, then dared to find answers and discover things others have not.

It is good to think there may be a place called Avalon, but first there's a lot of life to live and go for. To explore more of the world, and fit in all the projects hoped and planned, will require running in a high gear. All the same I kept my promise to my mother, stood by and up for her, and to brought things this far. In the event others in positions of power now finally start to act in the right ways, then I remain a kindred spirit for yet further adventures along the Distaval/ *Thalidomide* trail, and on the road ahead...

'The man who moves a mountain begins by carrying away small stones'

Confucius (551 – 479 B.C.) [3]

Thanks for reading, Paul.

Post Script and Authors Note

This is a space to acknowledge my mother, Margaret, a brilliant human being in so many ways. She worked for many years as a teacher supporting disadvantaged children with special needs, learning difficulties and physical impairments. Margaret was always good all-round company to be with; caring and nurturing as well as positive, cheerful, and well grounded. Her sewing skills were amazing and enabled cloths to be adapted for my reduced size, and now I realise how much extra love and care was put into all the adaptations.

At the same time my reductions in limb size and other impairments was not her fault, and thus *"16 Weeks and Everything After..."©* had to be written for her, and also for all the mothers who were misled on the potential of *Thalidomide* or other drugs to harm their babies. This is at any level, at any and all stages of pregnancy, in any year pre or post 1962. My expectations are *"16 Weeks and Everything After..."©* would be appreciated by her, and is another positive part of her legacy. People I have met along the way reinforce optimism *"16 Weeks and Everything After..."©* can contribute to the good for recognition of others globally, who have been negatively affected by the drug *Thalidomide*. It would be especially encouraging if it would also provide transferrable application to a broad range of contexts; including where other chemicals/processes maybe harming the environment, plus other drugs with questionable safety records that may have also not been satisfactorily concluded, leaving unresolved issues. All mothers want justice for all drugs that harmed babies.

Appendix

Chapter 6 Rebuilding Noah's Ark on a Coastal Footpath

Appendix Cubit measurement references can vary at the edges, but such tends to increase in size, not decrease. Searching for historical references I came up with studies by Gift, W (2001) [A] assessed the 'Modern Cubit' being at the smallest of 17 1/5" (43.75cm) at the low end, premised on the Modern Siloam Tunnel measurement at a total of 525m @ 1200 cubits. There are even longer cubit references from ancient times known as Royal Cubits [B], with inheritance to more African roots and range from 21 ¼" (517mm) to 22 ¼" (546mm).

Gitt, W., (2001), The Most Amazing Ship in the History of the World, Fundamentum, Germany, p. 7,2001 (German).437.5 mm (17.22 in) '0.4375m', p. 8. (For comparison, Gitt provided eight other cubits including the enormous 66.69cm Prussian cubit) Sourced from Modern Siloam Tunnel measurement (525m) compared to inscription of 1,200 cubits which gives 525/1200 = 0.4375m.

Marshall Clagett (1999). Ancient Egyptian science, a Source Book. Volume Three: Ancient Egyptian Mathematics. Philadelphia: American Philosophical Society. ISBN 978-0-87169-232-0.

Information Materials, Bibliography and References

Part I The Conscious informs the Subconscious

Chapter 1   *"Your Hands and Your Feet!"*
1. Marieb, E. N., (1992), Human Anatomy and Physiology, 2nd Edition, foetal development, The Benjamin/ Cummings Publishing Company, Inc. p991, basic diagram of a 16 weeks foetus
2. Emilia Earhart "The most difficult thing is the decision to act, the rest is merely tenacity"

Chapter 2   **Rebuilding Noah's Ark on a Coastal Footpath**
1. Oxford Latin Minidictionary, Latin – English, [edited by Moorwood, J.,] (1997), Oxford University Press, p69, p70
2. Cassell (First Ed. 1959©/ 5th Ed. 19th Impression 1987, reprint 1997) Latin Dictionary (Latin to English & English to Latin), Cassell Publications Ltd, Wellington House, 125 Strand, London, WC2R OBB [Dr. P. Simpson: MA. Assistant Master, Formerly Head of Classics Department at Eton College], p159, p505
3. Porter, J. R., The Illustrated Guide to the Bible, Oxford University Press, (1995), The Flood, p32–p33, p33 (italics), Noahs Ark, an illustration from the Nuremberg Bible of 1483, The subject of the Ark has been of much debate. In Genesis 6.15, God gives dimensions of Ark as 300 by 50 by 30 cubits (one cubit was about 18 inches or 45cm). This was often taken to mean that the vessel

was rectangular. N.B. The word "ark" in Hebrew, teba, means, "box" or "chest", and is otherwise used only for the basket in which the baby Moses was laid.

4. Goodreads, https://www.goodreads.com/quotes/915568-if-you-do-not-expect-the-unexpected-you-will-not

5. Andrew Loomis, Drawing for All its Worth, (1939 original ©/ 1946), p56

6. The Bible Old Testament; Genesis 6:15,

7. Porter, J. R., The Illustrated Guide to the Bible, Oxford University Press, (1995), The Flood, p32–p33, p33 (italics), Noahs Ark, an illustration from the Nuremberg Bible of 1483, The subject of the Ark has been of much debate. In Genesis 6.15, God gives dimensions of Ark as 300 by 50 by 30 cubits (one cubit was about 18 inches or 45 cm). This was often taken to mean that the vessel was rectangular. N.B. The word "ark" in Hebrew, teba, means, "box" or "chest", and is otherwise used only for the basket in which the baby Moses was laid.

8. Alcott, L., M. (1868 Vol. 1 1869 Vol.2), [1989/ 2010 3rd Edition], Little Women, Penguin Classics, Chapter 44, p456

Chapter 3   Growing Concerns

1. BBC News (2000), CJD fears over growth hormone http://news.bbc.co.uk/1/hi/health/2000032.stm

2. Collins Gem Dictionary of Quotations (1988), p256, Saki 1870-1916

3. England, M., A., (1996), Life Before Birth, Second Edition, Mosby – Wolfe, (an imprint of Times Mirror International Publications Limited), Normal Series of Development - The Fetal Period, p12 [photo illustration a, b and c] @ 16 Weeks development, p9, p12-14, p14

Weeks 20 development [photo illustration g] p14. & Head and Neck Development, The External Ear, p90-p92

4. VI Vademecum International, de Especialidades Farmaceuticas y Biologicas, Spetma Edicion Daimon Espania (1966), p319-230, (1969) p393 (1970) p415, (1971) p397 (1973) p434 (1975) p454

5. The Sunday Times 3rd May (2015), The Forgotten Victims, by Caroline Scott

6. Magazanik, M., (2015), Silent Shock (The men behind the *thalidomide* scandal and an Australian family's long road to justice, Text Publishing Melbourne Australia

7. Pers. Com. Michael Magazanik from History of *Thalidomide* Embryopathy p205

8. Sjostrom, H. & Nillson, R. (1972), *Thalidomide* and the Power of the Drug Companies, Penguin Books – (Handmade and printed in Great Britain by Hazell Watson & Viney Ltd)', p103-p104

9. Confucius: http://izquotes.com/quote/40959

Part II Deeper Realizations

Chapter 4   In the Deep End and Tri-ing new things

1. New Walk Museum & Art Gallery, Leicester, Leicester City Council, The Dinosaur Gallery – Exploring Lost Worlds, Charnia Fossil, named after Rodger Mason as Charnia Mason who discovered it in 1957

2. LetsRun.com The Greatest Race You've Never Heard of by Jonathan Gault (Feb 1 2015) http://www.letsrun. com/news/2015/01/greatest-race-youve-never-heard/

3. Scott Tinley full quote: http://www.quotemaster.org/ q3005b5756e6e766c73efc04a7cd87f2b

Chapter 5   Dairy or Diary

1. Sue Townsend (as Adrian Mole) (1982/ 1985) The Secret Diary of Adrian Mole Aged 13 ¾, Methuen Publishing
2. https://tinybuddha.com/wisdom-quotes/if-you-get-up-one-more-time-than-you-fall-you-will-make-it-through/

Chapter 6   Connection Mapping, by Mapping Connections

1. *Jpn J Psychiatry Neurol. 1987 Jun;41(2):197-205. Electroencephalographic study of 137 patients with* thalidomide *embryopathy. Kanno O*[1].
2. BBC online, 1988: Egg industry fury over salmonella claim, (Accessed 2015) http://news.bbc.co.uk/onthisday/hi/dates/stories/december/3/newsid_2519000/2519451.stm
3. Irlen syndrome history and founder http://irlen.com/founder-helen-irlen/
4. Marieb, E., N. [R.N., PhD. Holyoke Community College], (2001), Human Anatomy, (1995), p386-p390
5. England, M., A. & Wakely, j. (1991), A Colour Atlas of the BRAIN & SPINAL CORD (AN INTRODUCTION TO NORMAL NEUROANATOMY), Wolfe Publishing Ltd, *Embryology – Early Development, Flexures of the Brain,* p22–p25
6. England, M., A., (1983), A Colour Atlas of Life Before Birth: Normal Fetal Development – An Atlas of embryonic and Fetal development, Wolfe Medical Publications Ltd, (Printed by Grafos SA, Arte sobre Papel, Barcelona, Spain reprinted 1990), p54-p55, p54-p56 photo D Week13 Photo E Week 18 (7) Occipital lobe, p54-p59, p59 photos A – C., C Ref 13 Weeks 18, Occipital lobe (12)
7. England, M., A (1996), Life before Birth Second Ed., Mosby-Wolfe, inside first page, p54–p66, (p62), p112 [126a. Arteriogram of 122mm @ c.16weeks]

8. Alan Baddeley: phonological loop and language acquisition, You Tube; https://www.youtube.com/watch?v=ZQEHLqjJAhQ

9. Eysenck, M., W., Keane, M., T. (2002) First printed (2000), Cognitive Psychology, A Students Handbook, 4th edition, p156-p160, p534

10. Carlson, B., M. (2009), Human Embryology and Developmental Biology, Fourth Edition, Mosby Elsevier, [Bruce m. Carlson MD, PhD, Professor Emeritis, Department of Cell Developmental Biology, University of Michigan, Ann Arbor, Michigan] p267 Fig11.33

11. Carlson, N. R., (The University of Massachusetts) (1993), 4th Edition, Psychology the Science of Behaviour, Allyn And Bacon, p9

12. Hilgard E. J. (et al: - Atkinson, R. L,, Atkinson R. C., Smith, E. E., Bem, D. J., & Nolan-Hoeksema, S.) 1996 Introduction to Psychology 12th Ed., Harcourt Brace College Publishers, Chapter 2, p48, p51, p54-p55

13. BMJ 23rd January 1960 DCBL Distillers Company (Biochemicals) Limited, Broadwayhouse, The Broadway, Wimbledon, London, S. W. 19 Telephone: LIBerty 6600; - Double page spread advertisement, BRITISH MEDICAL JOURNAL, JAN. 23, 1960, 'DISTAVAL' IS SAFE

14. DCBL Distillers Company (Biochemicals) Limited, Broadwayhouse, The Broadway, Wimbledon, London, S. W. 19 Telephone: LIBerty 6600; advertisement for Valgraine c. 1961; Valgraine *The powerful new partnership against migraine", and "each tablet contains: Thalidomide ('Distaval'), 12.5mg, Ergotamine Tartrate B.P. 1.0mg"*

15. DCBL Distillers Company (Biochemicals) Limited,

Broadwayhouse, The Broadway, Wimbledon, London, S. W. 19 Telephone: LIBerty 6600; advertisement "AN OLD MANS RECOVERY, confirms the singular <u>safety</u> of 'DISTAVAL' THALIDOMIDE, in Proceedings of the Royal Society of Medicine, Vol. 53, No. 9, pp. Vii-ix Distaval Forte a *Thalidomide* super dose, quoted *"...the safe day time sedative which is equally safe in hypnotic doses by night, 'Distaval' is especially suitable for infants, the aged and patients under severe emotional stress."* [14]. Re; elderly man who somehow took a huge over dose without any harmful effects

16. BMJ on 24th June 1961 DCBL Distillers Company (Biochemicals) Limited, Broadwayhouse, The Broadway, Wimbledon, London, S. W. 19 Telephone: LIBerty 6600; - Double page spread advertisement, BRITISH MEDICAL JOURNAL, JUNE. 24, 1961, this child's life may depend on the safety of 'Distaval'

17. *Proc. Soc. Exp. Biol., N.Y..* 1962 109, 511 (cited in The Lancet, Letters to the Editor, 1116, November 24, 1962; Teratogenic Effects of *Thalidomide* in the Sprague Dawley Rat: - King, C.T.G. & Kendrick, F., J.)

18. Sjöstrom, H. & Nillsson, R. (1972), *Thalidomide* and the Power of the Drug Companies, Penguin Books (Handmade and printed in Great Britain by Hazell Watson & Viney Ltd)', p189-p191

19. Aristotle sometime between 384 BC and 322BC: Good Reads: http://www.goodreads.com/quotes/366890-if-you-would-understand-anything-observe-its-beginning-and-its

Chapter 7   Chasing Dragonflies and A Trip to 1968/ 69

1. Parker, S., (2007), The World Encyclopaedia of Fossil

Collecting, Arthropods insects, Lorenz Books © Annesss Publishing Ltd, p144)

2. .d' Aguilar, J. Dommanget J-L, Prechac, R. (1985/ 1986 English Translation), A Field Guide to the Dragonflies of Britain, Europe and North Africa, Collins, p17

3. Brooks & Askew (1999) A guide to dragonflies, and damselflies of Britain, FSC Publications with the Natural History Museum Text (1999), Dragonflies in context, p1, p2.

4. Field Studies Council Head Office Preston Montford, Shrewsbury, Shropshire SY4 1HW:- F.S.C. Publications contact: publications@field-studies-council.org

5. Wolterbeek, H.T. Garty, J. Reis, M.A Freitas M.C. (2003), Trace Metals and other Contaminants in the Environment, p377-p419

6. Cook, L. M. Mani G. S. and Varley M. E. *Post-industrial Melanism in the Peppered Moth*, Science, New Series, Vol. 231, No. 4738 (Feb. 7, 1986), pp. 611-613

7. Weyler, R., (2004), Green peace (How a group of ecologists, journalists, and visionaries changed the world), *Raincoast Books, Vancouver, British Columbia distributed by Holtzbrinck Publishers, p134, p575*

8. Ansell Adams, 1902–1984

Chapter 8   Unanswered Questions in Australia

1. THE DISTILLERS COMPANY BIO-CHEMICALS (Australia PTY) LIMITED, Campbell Street, Artarmon, N.S.W, 29th November 1961 + accompanying Circular N. 21, TO MATRONS OF ALL HOSPTIALS: WITHDRAWAL OF 'DISTAVAL', 8th December 1961. Available on line, Accessed 26/03/ 2015; (Distillers Company Bio-chemicals Ltd. Circular N. 21 (8th December 1961) with an accompanying letter dated 29th November 1961,

sent out by Distillers Company Bio Chemicals (Australia PTY) Limited, Campbell Street, Artamon, NSW, Australia), available from; health.wa.gov.au

2. DCBL Distillers Company (Biochemicals) Limited, Broadwayhouse, The Broadway, Wimbldon, London, S. W. 19 Telphone: LIBerty 6600; advertisement for Valgraine c. 1961; Valgraine *The powerful new partnership against migraine"*, and *"each tablet contains: Thalidomide ('Distaval'), 12.5mg, Ergotamine Tartrate B.P. 1.0mg"*

3. DCBL Distillers Company (Biochemicals) Limited, Broadwayhouse, The Broadway, Wimbledon, London, S. W. 19 Telphone: LIBerty 6600; advertisement "AN OLD MANS RECOVERY, confirms the singular safety of 'DISTAVAL' THALIDOMIDE, in Proceedings of the Royal Society of Medicine, Vol. 53, No. 9, pp. Vii-ix Distaval Forte a *Thalidomide* super dose, quoted *"...the safe day time sedative which is equally safe in hypnotic doses by night, 'Distaval' is especially suitable for infants, the aged and patients under severe emotional stress."* [14]. Re; elderly man who somehow took a huge over dose without any harmful effects

4. BMJ 23rd January 1960 DCBL Distillers Company (Biochemicals) Limited, Broadwayhouse, The Broadway, Wimbldon, London, S. W. 19 Telphone: LIBerty 6600; - Double page spread advertisement, BRITISH MEDICAL JOURNAL, JAN. 23, 1960, 'DISTAVAL' IS SAFE

5. BMJ on 24th June 1961 DCBL Distillers Company (Biochemicals) Limited, Broadwayhouse, The Broadway, Wimbledon, London, S. W. 19 Telphone: LIBerty 6600; - Double page spread advertisement, BRITISH MEDICAL JOURNAL, JUNE. 24, 1961, this child's life may depend on the safety of 'Distaval'

6. DCBL Distillers Company (Biochemicals) Limited, Broadwayhouse, The Broadway, Wimbledon, London, S. W. 19 Telphone: LIBerty 6600; advertisement for Distaval Forte c. 1961

7. Sherrin, N., (2004), I wish I'd Said That, Oxford University Press, *p3*

8. The Medicines Act of 1968

9. Compensation for *Thalidomide* Survivors April 2010 Report, Prepared for the Minister for Health and Children, by the State Claims Agency page 4, 13

10. Australia and yellow/ gold tablets. Quoting; *FJM LECTURE 1958, of "distaval forte" each contain 100 mg. thalidomide. The dose for hypnosis is one tablet at night. … "in South Australia, making 36 regional faculties in all, 25 … made in white and yellow gold by Messrs. Garrard and Co. Ltd., …". www.bmj.com/ content/2/5108/1349.full.pdf* **PDF - MEDBJIStrN**

11. Baker R and McKenzie N (July 27, 2012) http://www. dailyliberal.com.au/story/147371/australian-women-used-as-human-guinea-pigs/

12. Wilson, A., The Guardian Workers Weekly CPA, ISSN 1325 295X, #1566 September 26th 2012 pg5 "*Thalidomide* Apology Cold Comfort to Mother"

13. *Thalidomide* 1974; The 98 We Forgot, Published on May 18, 2014, ATV (Midlands Independent Television) – this documentary examines the effects of *thalidomide* and was first shown in 1974 through a well known *thalidomide* campaigner journalist John Pilger

14. Braithwaite, J., (1984) COPRPORATE CRIME in the pharmaceutical industry, Routledge & Kegan Paul, London, Boston, Melbourne and Henley, p73

15. ITV World in Action programme (1968) Dr Ronald Sandison at Powick Psychiatric Hospital in

Worcestershire Part 1 https://www.youtube.com/watch?v=UzjeBaBFWqwPart 2 https://www.youtube.com/watch?v=ZJU4X60ce30

16. Wortis, J (MD) Am J Psychiatry 119: 621 -626 January 1963, Psychopharmacology and physiological treatments, 1963, Review of psychiatric progress 1962, pg 621.

17. The Sydney Morning Herald, 27ᵗʰ July 2012, Australian women used as guinea pigs, by Richard Baker and Nick McKenzie, http://www.smh.com.au/national/australian-women-used-as-human-guinea-pigs-20120726-22voq.html

18. Knwoles, E., (2008), Quotations for occasions, Harper Collins Publishers, p134

Part III A Greater and Wider Awareness

Chapter 9   Joining Unseen dots…

1. Arthur Conan Doyle, "A Case of Identity" Sherlock Holmes

2. Sjostrom, H. & Nillson, R. (1972), *Thalidomide* and the Power of the Drug Companies, Penguin Books – (Handmade and printed in Great Britain by Hazell Watson & Viney Ltd), p103-p104

3. Ethan Hawke, Ash Wednesday, https://www.goodreads.com/quotes/706314-success-isn-t-measured-by-what-you-achieve-it-s-measured-by

Chapter 10   A Phone Call for Help out of a National Park

1. PEAK DISTRICT NATIONAL PARK, History of our National Park http://www.peakdistrict.gov.uk/learning-about/about-the-national-park/our-history

http://www.peakdistrict.gov.uk/__data/assets/pdf_
file/0004/494410/3459_Parklife_WEB.pdf

2. The – telephone –box, (2015) accessed (2015), Re: Kiosk
   No. 6, http://www.the-telephone-box.co.uk/kiosks/k6/

3. England, M., J (1973), An Atlas of Foetal and Embryonic
   Development, by Wolf Publications.

4. England, M., A. & Wakely, j. (1991), A Colour Atlas of
   the BRAIN & SPINAL CORD (AN INTRODUCTION TO
   NORMAL NEUROANATOMY), Wolfe Publishing Ltd,
   Embryology – Early Development, Flexures of the Brain
   p22-p25.

5. Brynner, R and Stevens, T., (2001) Dark Remedy, The
   impact of *Thalidomide* and its renewal as a vital
   medicine, Basic Books A member of the Perseus Book
   Group New York, p16, p41, p44

6. Sjostrom, H. & Nillson, R. (1972), *Thalidomide* and
   the Power of the Drug Companies, Penguin Books
   – (Handmade and printed in Great Britain by Hazell
   Watson & Viney Ltd), p121-p124, p121-p130

7. Green, D., M. (1996), Bendectin and Birth Defects, p78

8. The Sunday Times Insight Team, (Knightley, P., Evans, H.,
   Potter, E., Wallace, M.) (1979), Suffer The Children, The
   Story of Thalidomide, Futura Publications Ltd p68–p70

9. mBMJ (DEC 2 1961) p1499.

10. BBC Online Parkinson, J BBC News Magazine, 2015
    (Friday 24th April), The yard for red phone boxes
    that ring no more http://www.bbc.co.uk/news/
    magazine-32315904

11. The Oxford Dictionary of Quotations, 14th century proverb

Chapter 11 A Connection NOT to be missed at Aberdeen

1. Knwoles, E., (2008), Quotations for occasions, Harper
   Collins Publishers, p23, p40

2. Kobué, C (year Unknown) Florence and Tuscany, 2nd Edition, GLOBETROTTER, Travel Guide, New Holland Publishers (UK) Ltd, London, p8, p40-41, & p46

3. Sjostrom, H. & Nillson, R. (1972), *Thalidomide* and the Power of the Drug Companies, Penguin Books – (Handmade and printed in Great Britain by Hazell Watson & Viney Ltd), p121-p130, p164-p166, p176, p232-p235

4. Green, D., M. (1996), Bendectin and Birth Defects, University of Pennsylvania Press p78

5. The Sunday Times Insight Team, (Knightley, P., Evans, H., Potter, E., Wallace, M.) (1979), Suffer The Children - The Story of Thalidomide, Futura Publications Ltd p68–p70

6. Aberdeen University Press Release 2009, on line page last updated at 21:00 GMT, Monday 11 May 2009 22:00 UK, Scientist offers *thalidomide* Clue, Re; Work by Dr Neil Vargesson (Scientist claim they have finally worked out how and why the drug thalidomide caused limb defects in thousands of babies) Dr Neil Vargesson The University of Aberdeen School of Medical Sciences Senior Lecture, School of Medical Science Institute of Medical Sciences of Aberdeen, Fosterhill, Aberdeen AB25 2ZD, Scotland

7. Lawrence J Peter quote: https://www.brainyquote.com/quotes/quotes/l/laurencej137325.html

Chapter 12   Life is Stranger than Fiction

1. Lewington, A., (2003), Plants For People, eden project books, Transworld Publishers p61-63 Uxbridge Road, London W5 5SA, p186, p214, p286-p288

2. Tudge, C., (2005), The secret life of trees how they live and why they matter, Penguin Books, p177, 178

Chapter 13   A single Lightning Bolt out of the Bluest of Skies

1. Malvern Hills Conservators, Geology. http://www.
   malvernhills.org.uk/visiting/geology_and_geography.
   aspx

2. Flint (FSRA), C., (2010) The Pictorial Guide to The
   Malvern Hills, Book One, Published by Malvern Walks
   and Printed in Great Britain by Aldine Print Limited,
   Barnards Green Road, Malvern WR14 3NB, p10

3. Knwoles, E., (2008), Quotations for occasions, Harper
   Collins Publishers, p155

4. England, M., J (1973), An Atlas of Foetal and Embryonic
   Development, by Wolf Publications

5. England, M., A. & Wakely, j. (1991), A Colour Atlas of
   the BRAIN & SPINAL CORD (AN INTRODUCTION TO
   NORMAL NEUROANATOMY), Wolfe Publishing Ltd,
   Embryology – Early Development, Flexures of the Brain,
   p22-25

6. European Commission of Human Rights, Application
   No. 6538/74 Times Newspapers Ltd and others against
   United Kingdom, Based on The Times Newspaper
   Investigations, p124, p139-142

7. J. Neurol. Neurosurg. Psychiat., 1960, 23, 56., A RATING
   SCALE FOR DEPRESSION, HAMILTON, MAX, From
   the Department of Psychiatry, University of Leeds,
   APPENDIX 1 AND 2 ASSESSMENT OF DEPRESSION

8. Sir Alan Marre Report 1978, *Thalidomide* – 'Y' List Inquiry
   HMSO, Department of Health and Social Security,
   (Section 68) Evidence of Access pg17.

9. Mark Twain: https://www.brainyquote.com/quotes/
   quotes/m/marktwain109630.html

Part IV Shining daylight into Some Very Dark Corners

Chapter 14   Finally Coming Home via Hollywood and Colorado

1. Toms, L., G., (2009) Managing Global Enterprise Risks, iUniverse, Inc. New York Bloomington p38; Winston Churchill quote
2. The Sunday Times Insight Team, (Knightley, P., Evans, H., Potter, E., Wallace, M.) (1979), Suffer The Children - The Story of Thalidomide, Futura Publications Ltd, p98
3. Bryner, R., Stevens, T., (2001), Dark Remedy, Basic Books – Member of the Perseus Book Group New York, p42
4. The First Seal Baby - The Real Story of Thalidomide, http://healthworldnet.com/best-of-the-best/The-First-Seal-Baby-The-Real-Story-of-Thalidomide/?C=8439
5. Carpenter, D., (2010) Reputation & Power (Organisational Image and Pharmaceutical Regulation Image), p246, p257, p347, p346-p349
6. Tea Wisdom, Arton Fisher (2009) Tuttle Publishing
7. LifeART (and/or) Mediclips images copyright 2008 Wolters Kluwer Health – Lippincott Williams and Wilkins, Foetal Skull development weeks 12, 16 & Full term
8. Tom Stoppard http://quoteaddicts.com/940224
9. Andy Warhol, http://izquotes.com/quote/193372

Chapter 15   Nature Never Hides or Misrepresents Anything

1. WESTONBIRT The National Arboretum, Growing Green Activity Pack – The Trunk, Tree trunks – general facts and information
2. CNN, June 30, 2010, Study links bee decline to cell phones, by Sasha Herriman Accessed November 2016 on line: http://edition.cnn.com/2010/WORLD/

europe/06/30/bee.decline.mobile.phones/

3. BBC R4 News Thursday 29th June 2017 Inside Science 21:00- 21:30hrs/ Rebecca Morrelle Science Correspondent Bees and Neonicatoides

4. Thomas Huxley, English Biologist 1825-1895 https://www.mindfueldaily.com/livewell/never-give-up-5-quotes-on-tenacity-to-push-you-further

5. Sjostrom, H. & Nillson, R. (1972), *Thalidomide* and the Power of the Drug Companies, Penguin Books – (Handmade and printed in Great Britain by Hazell Watson & Viney Ltd), p112-p130

6. England, M., A., (1983), A Colour Atlas of Life Before Birth: Normal Fetal Development – An Atlas of embryonic and Fetal development, Wolfe Medical Publications Ltd, (Printed by Grafos SA, Arte sobre Papel, Barcelona, Spain reprinted 1990), p23 photo B+C, p54-p65, p172-p173

7. England, M., A. & Wakely, j. (1991), A Colour Atlas of the BRAIN & SPINAL CORD (AN INTRODUCTION TO NORMAL NEUROANATOMY), Wolfe Publishing Ltd, Embryology – Early Development, Flexures of the Brain p22-25.

8. England, M., A., (1996), 2nd Edition, Life Before Birth: Normal Fetal Development [Paperback], Mosby – Wolfe, Times Mirror International Publishers Limited, (c) England, M., A., (1973), Life Before Birth: Normal Fetal Development – An Atlas of embryonic and Fetal development, Wolfe Publishing Ltd, Normal Series of Development - The Fetal Period, p12 [photo illustration b and c] @ 16 Weeks development, p9 p12-14, p14. & Head and Neck Development, The External Ear, p90-92, p197 (j) (k)@14 weeks p198(m) (n) (o) @16 weeks p54-63, p178

9. King, C.T.G. & Kendrick. F. J. (1962) National Institute of Dental Research, National Institutes of Health, Bethesda, Maryland, Conducted with Kevedon branded *Thalidomide* supplied by Merrell Company: - Reported in The Lancet 1116 November 24, 1962 Letters to the Editor "Terratogenic Effects of *Thalidomide* in the Sprague Dawley Rat"

10. LifeART (and/or) Mediclips images copyright 2008 Wolters Kluwer Health – Lippincott Williams and Wilkins, Foetal Skull development weeks 12, 16 & Full term

11. Hutchinson, M., Mallatt, J., Marieb, E. N., and Wilhelm, P. B., (Photographs by Hutchings, R. T., and Zanetti, N. (2007), A Breif Atlas of Human Body Person Benjamin Cummings, p28-29, p43, p98, p100-103

12. Marieb, E., N. [R.N., PhD. Holyoke Community College], (2001), Human Anatomy, (1995) p386-p390, p182

13. Anson, B., J. Ph.D., Blast, T., H. Ph.D. and Richany, S., F., M.S. (December 20 1954), Department of Anatomy of the University of Wisconsin and the Department of North western University Medical School Contribution No. 615, p32 (pdf)

14. Carlson, B. M., (2009) ©, Human Embryology and Developmental Biology, Mosely Elsevier, p326 Fig.14.1

15. Ulijaszek, S. J., Johnson, F. E., Preece, M., A. (1998) The Cambridge Encyclopeida of Human Growth and Development, Cambridge University Press, p420

16. Vargesson, Neil. (2009), "Thalidomide-induced Limb Defects: Resolving a 50-year-old Puzzle." BioEssays 31 (2009): 1327?36 (b) Aberdeen University Press Release 2009, on line page last updated at 21:00 GMT, Monday 11 May 2009 22:00 UK, Scientist offers *thalidomide* Clue, Re; Work by Dr Neil Vargesson (Scientist claim

they have finally worked out how and why the drug *thalidomide* caused limb defects in thousands of babies) Dr Neil Vargesson The University of Aberdeen School of Medical Sciences Senior Lecture, School of Medical Science Institute of Medical Sciences of Aberdeen, Fosterhill, Aberdeen AB25 2ZD, Scotland

17. Silent Spring, By Carlson, R., (1962/ 1965), (50th Anniversary Edition 2015)

Chapter 16   A Corporate Garden Path

1. Magazanik, M, (2015) Silent Shock, Text Publishing Melbourne Australia, p36-p37, p33-57 p58-p60, p96-p100, p136-137, p195-p207, p198-p199, p200, p214, p217

2. Knightley, P., Evans, H., Potter, E., Wallace, M., (1980) [© 1979 by The Times Newspapers Ltd] –, Suffer the Children the Sunday Times Insight Team, Future Publications Ltd, p14-p20, p27-p39, p72, p82-p89, p96-98, p98, p101, p145, p343, p361

3. Sjostrom, H. & Nillson, R. (1972), Thalidomide and the Power of the Drug Companies, Penguin Books – (Handmade and printed in Great Britain by Hazell Watson & Viney Ltd, p46-p47,p59-p65. p99-p104, p113-p121, p156, p175, p182-p184, p188-p190, p209, p210

4. Somers, G., F., [Distillers Co. (Bio-Chemicals) Ltd, Speke, Liverpool], The Lancet, 912, April 28 1962 "Thalidomide and Congenital Abnormalities"

5. Bryner, R., Stevens, T., (2001), Dark Remedy, Basic Books – Member of the Perseus Book Group New York, p12, p16, p23-p24, p41, p145-p148, p166

6. The Lancet, Letters to the Editor (552 March 9, 1963), Teratogenic effects of Thalidomide and related

substances, Boylen, B., J., Horn, H., H. & Johnson, W., J. Biochemistry Department, Frank W. Horner Limited., Montreal, Canada

7. The Lancet, Letters to the Editor (772 April 6, 1963), Teratogenic effects of Thalidomide, Enmann, B., Universitast-Kinderklinik, Cologne

8. Lucy, J. F., and Behrman, R.E., (1963), Thalidomide: effects on pregnancy in the rhesus monkey, *Science 139: 1295-96*

9. Delahunt, C. S., and Lassen, L. J., (1964), Thalidomide' syndrome in monkeys. *Science 146: 1300 and 1305- ; Kiss, N., Feldman, E., and Oaks, M. (1965); Some comparative pharmacological studies in man and the monkey with thalidomide. Toxicol. Appl. Pharmacol. 7: 481-82*

10. Hendrickx, A. G., Axelrod, L. R., and Clayborn, L. D., (1966) 'Thalidomide' syndrome in baboons. *Nature 210: 958-59*

11. Somers (1962) and Sellers (1962) cited in; King, C.T.G. & Kendrick. F. J. (1962) National Institute of Dental Research, National Institutes of Health, Bethesda, Maryland, Conducted with Kevedon branded Thalidomide supplied by Merrell Company: - Reported in The Lancet 1116 November 24, 1962 Letters to the Editor "Terratogenic Effects of Thalidomide in the Sprague Dawley Rat"

12. Sir Alan Marre Report 1978, Thalidomide -'Y' List Inquiry HMSO, Department of Health and Social Security

13. The Lancet, (1134 May 21, 1966), Preliminary Communications, Minor Ocular Abnormalities associated with Thalidomide, Stanley Cant, J, Tennent Institute of Ophthalmology

14. England, M., A., (1996), 2nd Edition, Life Before Birth: Normal Fetal Development [Paperback], Mosby – Wolfe, Times Mirror International Publishers Limited, (c) England, M., A., (1973), Life Before Birth: Normal Fetal Development – An Atlas of embryonic and Fetal development, Wolfe Publishing Ltd, p8 photo10a-d, p2-p9

15. Vargesson, Neil. (2009), "Thalidomide-induced Limb Defects: Resolving a 50-year-old Puzzle." BioEssays 31 (2009): 1327?36 (b) Aberdeen University Press Release 2009, on line page last updated at 21:00 GMT, Monday 11 May 2009 22:00 UK, Scientist offers thalidomide Clue, Re; Work by Dr Neil Vargesson (Scientist claim they have finally worked out how and why the drug thalidomide caused limb defects in thousands of babies) Dr Neil Vargesson The University of Aberdeen School of Medical Sciences Senior Lecture, School of Medical Science Institute of Medical Sciences of Aberdeen, Fosterhill, Aberdeen AB25 2ZD, Scotland

16. Scott Tinley: http://www.azquotes.com/quote/795428

17. Pilger, J., (1986), Heroes, Publisher: Jonathan Cape Ltd, 32 Bedford Square, London WC1B 3EL, Chapter 6 A little bit of humanity, p67-p73

18. Thalidomide 1974; The 98 We Forgot, Published on May 18, 2014, ATV (Midlands Independent Television) – this documentary examines the effects of thalidomide and was first shown in 1974 through a well known thalidomide campaigner journalist John Pilger

19. Jurand, A., (1966) Early changes in limb buds of chick embryos after thalidomide treatment, *j. Embryol. Exp. Morpho*l. 16; 289-300

20. BMJ. 2006 Sep 9; 333(7567): 554 Obituaries, Ernest Philip Quibell by Gillian T McCarthy Accessed: https://

www.ncbi.nlm.nih.gov/pmc/articles/PMC1562519/
Extended version: file:///C:/Users/DELL%20User/
Downloads/bmj_333_7567_554-a__1.pdf

21. Harold Evans (2015/ 2016) film; *"Attacking the Devil –
The last Nazi War Crime"* shown on Netflics

22. The Telegraph, Thalidomide 50 years on: 'Justice
has never been done and it burns away', by Martin
Fletcher 8:00 GMT 07 Jan 2016; http://www.telegraph.
co.uk/news/health/12082527/Thalidomide-50-years-
on-Justice-has-never-been-done-and-it-burns-away.
html

23. Mat Frazer, Happy Birthday Thalidomide, (2015) DVD

24. Magazanik, M, (2015) / (2016) Video's (a) Thalidomide's
link to Nazi Germany, https://www.youtube.com/
watch?v=tXuMslDAJts + (b) The risks of medicating
pregnant women, https://www.youtube.com/
watch?v=1O9hPWbrlHE + (c) Silent Shock, https://
www.youtube.com/watch?v=nd7UYRcSA9c taken
from: The Conversation, December 8, 2015, 7:11pm
GMT, http://theconversation.com/nazis-lies-and-
spying-private-detectives-how-thalidomides-maker-
avoided-justice-51730

25. Mückter (1965) Antimicrobial agents and
Chemotherapy-1965, Copyright © 1966 American
Society for Microbiology printed in USA. Thalidomide
and Tumor, H. Mückter; Research Laboratories,
Chemie Gruthenthal GmbH, Stolberg/Rhineland,
Germany (1965); Available from: The British Library
Document Supply Service, Boston Spa, Wetherby,
United Kingdom LS23 7BQ bldss.bl.uk

26. Mark Twain quote: https://www.brainyquote.com/
quotes/quotes/m/marktwain122862.html

27. A life Redirected a Story of Human Illness, Consensus

and Canaries About Medical Science and its Loyalties (2003), Two articles by Karl-Erik Tallamo, p87 (pdf Karl-Erik Tallamo, Nissus Publishing, 2003

28. Oldham F., and Kelsey F. (1943); Studies on Anti-malarial Drugs: the Influence of Pregnancy on the Quinine Oxidase of Rabbit Liver by Francis K. Oldham and F. E. Kelsey, Journal of Pharmacology and Experimental Therapeutics p79 (1943) p81

29. Rice, E., (2007) 'Dr. Frances Kelsey: Turning the Thalidomide Tragedy into Food and Drug Administration Reform, Research Paper Senior Division © 2007, p6

30. Einstein quote: https://www.brainyquote.com/search_results.

31. D'Amato, R. J., Longhnan, M. S., Flynn, E., J., (1994) "Thalidomide is an inhibitor of angiogenesis. *Proc Nat Acad Sci USA 1994; 91: 4082-4085.*

32. Tinker Tailor Soldier Spy © (2011) Studio Canal Ltd, produced by Thomas Afredson, DVD 1hour 33-34mins

Chapter 17   Some Help from April fools

1. BBC ON THIS DAY: 31st March 1966: Harold Wilson Wins Sweeping Victory: http://news.bbc.co.uk/onthisday/hi/dates/stories/march/31/newsid_4693000/4693142.stm

2. Knightley, P., Evans, H., Potter, E., Wallace, M., (1980) [© 1979 by The Times Newspapers Ltd], Suffer the Children the Sunday Times Insight Team, Future Publications Ltd, p11, p99-p100, p183-p191, p189-p193, p190

3. Bryner, R., Stevens, T., (2001), Dark Remedy, Basic Books – Member of the Perseus Book Group New York, p12 p41, p43, p43-p44, p80-p81

4. Sjostrom, H. & Nillson, R. (1972), Thalidomide and the Power of the Drug Companies, Penguin Books,

Handmade and printed in Great Britain by Hazell Watson & Viney Ltd, p225

5. BMJ 23rd January 1960 DCBL Distillers Company (Biochemicals) Limited, Broadwayhouse, The Broadway, Wimbledon, London, S. W. 19 Telephone: LIBerty 6600; - Double page spread advertisement, BRITISH MEDICAL JOURNAL, JAN. 23, 1960, 'DISTAVAL' IS SAFE, (b) DCBL Distillers Company (Biochemicals) Limited, Broadwayhouse, The Broadway, Wimbledon, London, S. W. 19 Telephone: LIBerty 6600; advertisement for Valgraine c. 1961; Valgraine *The powerful new partnership against migraine"*, and *"each tablet contains: Thalidomide ('Distaval'), 12.5mg, Ergotamine Tartrate B.P. 1.0mg"* (c) DCBL Distillers Company (Biochemicals) Limited, Broadwayhouse, The Broadway, Wimbledon, London, S. W. 19 Telephone: LIBerty 6600; advertisement "AN OLD MANS RECOVERY, confirms the singular safety of 'DISTAVAL' THALIDOMIDE, in Proceedings of the Royal Society of Medicine, Vol. 53, No. 9, pp. Vii-ix Distaval Forte a Thalidomide super dose, quoted *"...the safe day time sedative which is equally safe in hypnotic doses by night, 'Distaval' is especially suitable for infants, the aged and patients under severe emotional stress."* (14). Re; elderly man who somehow took a huge over dose without any harmful effects (d) BMJ on 24th June 1961 DCBL Distillers Company (Biochemicals) Limited, Broadwayhouse, The Broadway, Wimbledon, London, S. W. 19 Telephone: LIBerty 6600; - Double page spread advertisement, BRITISH MEDICAL JOURNAL, JUNE. 24, 1961, this child's life may depend on the safety of 'Distaval'

6. Council of Europe 1977 May, European Commission of

Human Rights 6538/74; p14, p130, p134, p139, p142

7. Evans, H., (2009) 'My Paper Chase', thelittlebrown.co.uk chapter 15 Children in Our Conscience, p313, p314, p314-p318, p336

8. Nulsen, R., O. (1961), *"Trial of thalidomide in insomnia associated with the third trimester"*, American Journal of Obstetrics and Gynaecology, 81 (June 1961): 1245-8

9. Ashley, J., (1973©) Third Edition (1974), Journey into Silence, The Bodley Head Ltd, p124, p127, p134, p136-p137

10. Eayrs, G., J. Diplomacy and its Discontents, (1971), Political Science, p198; Mark Twain quote, *"History doesn't repeat its self but it rhymes"*

11. Thalidomide Victims Association of Canadian web site, (7 May 1999), Warren, R, The many faces of Thalidomide from (1957-1966) compiled by Randolph Warren, http://www.thalidomide.ca/many-faces-of-thalidomide/

12. Magazanik, M, (2015) Silent Shock, Text Publishing Melbourne Australia, p233

Part V Turning Negatives into Positives

Chapter 18   A Heroine and Betsy Andreu's good example

1. Knightley, P., Evans, H., Potter, E., Wallace, M., (1980) [© 1979 by The Times Newspapers Ltd] –, Suffer the Children the Sunday Times Insight Team, Future Publications Ltd, p99-p100, p100, p104

2. Carpenter, D., (2010) Reputation & Power (Organisational Image and Pharmaceutical Regulation Image), p 246, p257, p347

3. Rice, E., (2007) 'Dr. Frances Kelsey: Turning the Thalidomide Tragedy into Food and Drug Administration

Reform, Research Paper Senior Division © 2007, p6, p8

4. Oldham F., and Kelsey F. (1943); Studies on Anti-malarial Drugs: the Influence of Pregnancy on the Quinine Oxidase of Rabbit Liver by Francis K. Oldham and F. E. Kelsey, Journal of Pharmacology and Experimental Therapeutics (1943) p79, p81.

5. Bryner, R., Stevens, T., (2001), Dark Remedy, Basic Books – Member of the Perseus Book Group New York, p17, p40, p41, p45, p49, p54

6. Sjostrom, H. & Nillson, R. (1972), Thalidomide and the Power of the Drug Companies, Penguin Books – (Handmade and printed in Great Britain by Hazell Watson & Viney Ltd, p114-p116, p115, p210

7. Florence, Dr., A., L., (1961), BMJ, February 23rd 1961, p1954, Dr A. Leslie Florence, 'Is Thalidomide to Blame?'

8. The Sunday Times, (3rd May 2015), The Forgotten Victims, by Caroline Scott

9. O' Reilly, E., (2014), The Race to Truth, Transworld Publishers, p173, p235

10. The Program Studio Canal (2015) Directed by Steven Fears, 1hour 44 minutes staring

11. Macur, J. – (of the New York Times) (2014), Cycle of Lies, The Fall of Lance Armstrong, p82–p88, p378-p380

12. CNN 360°, (17 January 2013) Cooper, A., Anderson Cooper Live, 22:00hrs US Time, Betsy Andreu Live with Anderson Cooper http://ac360.blogs.cnn.com/2013/01/17besty-andreu-furious-at-armstrong/

13. The Telegraph (October 24th 2012), Lance Armstrong is a bully. I could not let the bully win, says whistle-blower Betsy Andreu, by Jacqueline Magnay

Chapter 19   A Zeitgeist Lens for Action

1. Worcester Cathedral 2015 Magna Carta Exhibition, Christianity and Culture June 2015 Worcester WR1 England

2. BBC, (2016) The making of Magna Carta by Dr David Starkey, Accessed: http://www.bbc.co.uk/programmes/p02hscbf

3. National Trust: https://www.nationaltrust.org.uk/runnymede/features/ankerwycke

4. Woodlands Trust, Yew Tree: https://www.woodlandtrust.org.uk/visiting-woods/trees-woods-and-wildlife/british-trees/native-trees/yew/

5. Mitchell, A., & Dadhania, M. (2003) A S Level Law, Cavendish Publishing Ltd, p232-p233, p247 p250, p250-p251, p252

6. NO Limits – History's Greatest Drug Scandal, Academy Award Winning Director John Zaritsky, (2015/ 2016) download p13, Monika Eisenberg Thalidomide survivor and campaigner

7. The Guardian (Friday 14th November 2014); "Thalidomide: how men who blighted the lives of thousands evaded justice", by Harold Evans

8. Magazanik, M, (2015) Silent Shock, Text Publishing Melbourne Australia, p233

9. Likesuccess.com

10. Knightley, P., Evans, H., Potter, E., Wallace, M., (1980) [© 1979 by The Times Newspapers Ltd] –, Suffer the Children the Sunday Times Insight Team, Future Publications Ltd, p269, p294-p313

11. Evans, H., (2009) 'My Paper Chase', thelittlebrown.co.uk chapter 15 Children in Our Conscience, p 294-p313, p335

12. Distillers Co. (Bio-chemicals) Ltd. v Thompson [1971] AC 458

13. Law Conflict of Laws LAWS2212 Semester 2, 2007
14. "All substances are poisons; there is none that is not a poison. The right dose differentiates a poison and a remedy" Paracelsus, 'Father of Toxicology' (1493-1541)
15. The Offices Shops and Railways Act (1963) (O.S.R.A. 1963), & Parts: 3, 20, Pdf available: http://www.legislation.gov.uk/ukpga/1963/41
16. The Health and Safety at Work Act 1974., statutory information available: http://www.hse.gov.uk/legislation/hswa.htm Parts 33, Information available: http://www.hse.gov.uk/enforce/enforcementguide/court/sentencing-penalties.htm
17. Health and Safety Commission Amendments of HSWA Section 28 to bring in line with Freedom of Information Act 2000
18. Bryner, R., Stevens, T., (2001), Dark Remedy, Basic Books – Member of the Perseus Book Group New York, p109
19. Micheal Magazanik, NO Limits Trailer A Film by John Zaritsky on Documentary Channel http://thalidomidestory.com/story/film/trailer/
20. Magna Carta 1215

Chapter 20   Knowledge Sharing

1. Peter Ducker; http://izquotes.com/quote/53235
2. Pers. Com. Gary Skyner 2017, correspondence from Manager Steven 19th May 2017, 11:50
3. ITV News, (18 September 2014), Claims of a cover up following the death of a Thalidomide baby borne more than 50 years ago, Accessed: http://www.itv.com/news/calendar/update/2014-09-18/claims-of-a-cover-up-over-the-death-of-a-thalidomide-baby-born-more-

than-fifty-years-ago/

4. The Guardian (Friday 14th November 2014) Thalidomide: how men who blighted the lives of thousands evaded justice, by Harold Evans

5. Mat Frazer, Happy Birthday Thalidomide, (2015) DVD Thalidomide UK, video/ DVD (2014) Happy Birthday Thalidomide 48mins, Presented by Matt Frazer – Thalidomide survivor, actor and Musician; Accessed Youtube: https://www.youtube.com/watch?v=Uv39wavt-ME

6. The Sunday Telegraph (Sunday 19th March 2017), *'How can we still be waiting for justice?'* by Jason Farrell

7. Primodos: The Secret Drug Scandal. An investigagion into the pregnacy drug. Presented by Jason Farrell, (Scheduled for Wednesday 22nd March 2017, 21:00hrs Sky Live but show later due to events that day at Westminster.) Shown during the week of 20th March 2017 also available on utube https://www.youtube.com/watch?v=7ZRkCNUQvBA

8. Financial Times September 14th 2016, *"Bayer braced for tough scrutiny over $66Billion Monsanto deal"*, by Arash Massoudi in London and James Fontanella-Kharn in New York and Guy Chazan in Berlin; Available on line; https://www.ft.com/content/e02ef0d4-7a6e-11e6-ae24-f193b105145e

9. Inman, B., (1999), Dont Tell The Paitent, pXII, p27

10. England, M., A (1996), Life before Birth Second Ed., Mosby-Wolfe

11. Sjostrom, H. & Nillson, R. (1972), Thalidomide and the Power of the Drug Companies, Penguin Books – (Handmade and printed in Great Britain by Hazell Watson & Viney Ltd, p46-p47, p188-p190, p209-p210

12. Bryner, R., Stevens, T., (2001), Dark Remedy, Basic

Books – Member of the Perseus Book Group New York, p41

13. Mückter (1965) Antimicrobial agents and Chemotherapy-1965, Copyright © 1966 American Society for Microbiology printed in USA. Thalidomide and Tumor, H. Mückter; Research Laboratories, Chemie Gruthenthal GmbH, Stolberg/Rhineland, Germany (1965); Available from: The British Library Document Supply Service, Boston Spa, Wetherby, United Kingdom LS23 7BQ, bldss.bl.uk

14. Sky News: Thursday 16th November 2017, Primodos: MPs attack 'white wash' report report into deformity drug, By Jason Farrell, Senior Political Correspondent https://news.sky.com/story/primodos-mps-attack-whitewash-report-into-deformity-drug-11128902

15. Sky News, Primodos: Wednesday 15th November 2017, Report into "Deformity Drug" Criticised ahead of release, By Jason Farrell, Senior Political Correspondent, https://news.sky.com/story/primodos-report-into-deformity-drug-criticised-ahead-of-release-11127149

16. The Gaurdian, Thursday 16th November 2017, Primodos pregacy test report criticised as 'white wash' by MP's https://www.theguardian.com/science/2017/nov/16/primodos-pregnancy-test-report-criticised-whitewash-mps

17. Ralph Adam Fine (1972), *The Great Drug Deception, The Shocking Story of MER/29 and the Folks Who Gave you Thalidomide,* Stein and Day Publishers New York

18. BBC R4 Desert Island Discs Sunday 16th October 2016 presented by Kirsty Young

19. BBC Radio 4 World at One, 26th September 2017 + BBC Health; We've had no help – epilepsy drug victims, by

Nick Triggle Health Correspondent accessed online: http://www.bbc.co.uk/news/health-41399848

20. Hansard: Valproate and Foetal Anticonvulsant Syndrome, 19 October 2017, Volume 629, Accessed online; https://hansard.parliament. uk/commons/2017-10-19/debates/84D4BB19-D2BF-446A-A249-CD28BD7E8E06/ ValproateAndFoetalAnticonvulsantSyndrome

21. BBC R4 The Today Programme, Friday 20th October 2017 06:00-09:00 hours

22. BBC Radio (4, 14 and 21 March 2016), Saving Science from the Scientists, by Alok Jha, (Producer Faizal Farook) http://www.bbc.co.uk/programmes/b07378cr

23. BBC Radio 4, Analysis (Monday 21 March 2016) 20:30-21:00 hours, Corporate Amnesia by Phil Tinline

24. Colenso, M., (2000), Kaizen strategies for successful organisational change - evolution and revolution in the organisation, Financial times–Pretence Hall

Chapter 21   C. S. R. – Having Cake and Eating It?

1. Toms, L., G., (2009) Managing Global Enterprise Risks, iUniverse, Inc. New York Bloomington p38; Douglas Barlow, "All management is risk management"

2. NHS England Publications Gateway Reference 03689, (14 July 2015) The use of medicines in people with learning disabilities; signed Dr Dominic Slowie National Clinical Director for Learning Disability and Dr Keith Ridge CBE Chief Pharmaceutical Officer

3. STATNews.com (JANUAURY 4, 2016) No time for stodgy: Crusading editor (Dr Fiona Godlee as BMJ chief editor) to shake things up in science, by Mark Pelow https:// www.statnews.com/2016/01/04/bmj-editor-fiona-godlee/

4. Peter Drucker; http://izquotes.com/quote/53227

5. BBC R4 File on Four NHS Whistle blowers Tuesday 7th February 2017 @ 20:00 to 20:30 hours, Reporter: Simon Cox, Producer Nicola Dowling

6. Peter ducker quote: https://www.brainyquote.com/quotes/peter_drucker_134881

7. John Pilger ATV Correspondent, (1974) Thalidomide – The Ninety Eight we forgot 1974 available on Youtube: https://www.youtube.com/watch?v=oXd9cokuQzw

8. Pilger, J., (1986), Heroes, Jonathan Cape, p67-p73

9. Mückter (1965) Antimicrobial agents and Chemotherapy-1965, Copyright © 1966 American Society for Microbiology printed in USA. Thalidomide and Tumor, H. Mückter; Research Laboratories, Chemie Grünenthal GmbH, Stolberg/Rhineland, Germany (1965); Available from: The British Library Document Supply Service, Boston Spa, Wetherby, United Kingdom LS23 7BQ, bldss.bl.uk

10. BBC (May 15th 2014) Thalidomide The Fifty Year Fight BBC documentary, Narrated by Juliet Stevenson, Edited by Gareth Williams Researcher Tobias Arndt produced and Directed by Stuart Strckson Story Vault Films for BBC; BBC Thalidomide – The 50 Year Fight Accessed on Youtube Accessed 30/4/2107 https://www.youtube.com/watch?v=fdLDmQTBHFY

11. Evans, H., (2009) 'My Paper Chase', thelittlebrown.co.uk chapter 15 Children in Our Conscience, p314-p337, p314-318, p332-p336, p333

12. Alan Marre Report 1978 *Thalidomide* – 'Y' List Inquiry HMSO, Department of Health and Social Security

13. Magazanik, M, (2015) Silent Shock, Text Publishing Melbourne Australia, 17, p199-p200

14. Reuters, (Sun March 16, 2014) Guinness pulls out

of NY's St. Patrick's Day parade over ban on gays: Accessed 30/4/ 2017: http://www.reuters.com/article/ us-usa-boston-st-patricks-idUSBREA2F0HY20140317

15. Mat Frazer, Happy Birthday Thalidomide, (2015) DVD Thalidomide UK, video/ DVD (2014) Happy Birthday Thalidomide 48mins, Presented by Matt Frazer – Thalidomide survivor, actor and Musician; Accessed Youtube: https://www.youtube.com/ watch?v=Uv39wavt-ME

16. WTDDTY, July 24th 2017, Young women still being prescribed thalidomide, by Bryan Hubbard, accessed at; https:// wddty.com/news/2017/07/young-women-still-being-prescribed-thalidomide.html?utm_source=Boomtrain&utm_medium=email&utm_campaign=enews_25072017&bt_ee=nFPQZuLpunkdBkWJh0Sf9vqOqyvPh5WalGdXpHgnZcrlYsiL/ VzHXAUisgnOwDjf&bt_ts=1500981966950 (Source: www.preventionofthalidomidebirthsineurope.com)

17. No Limits Down load http://thalidomidestory.com/wp-content/uploads/2016/05/No-Limits-press-kit-FINAL-April14.pdf p14

18. Micheal Magazanik, NO Limits Trailer A Film by John Zaritsky on Documentary Channel http:// thalidomidestory.com/story/film/trailer/

19. Knightley, P., Evans, H., Potter, E., Wallace, M., (1980) [© 1979 by The Times Newspapers Ltd] –, Suffer the Children the Sunday Times Insight Team, Future Publications Ltd, p183-p191

20. Richard Hooker quote: Cited in NICE, Professor Gillian Leng CBE, Deputy Chief Executive and Director of Health, Social Care, Nice. In Slide share #18, Accessed at https://www.slideshare.net/openforumevents/ professor-gillian-leng-cbe-deputy-chief-executive-and-director-of-health-and-social-care-nice

Chapter 22   The Road Ahead...

1. King Arthur of England http://www.glastonburyabbey.com/king_arthur_avalon.php
2. Avalon https://www.lonelyplanet.com/great-britain/travel-tips-and-articles/king-arthur-in-britain-where-to-find-the-truth-behind-the-legend
3. Confucius (551-479 B.C.): https://successstory.com/quote/confucius